Study Guide for
Health
and
Social Care
Support Workers

NVQ/SVQ In Care
Level 3 Core Units

Stephen O'Kell

First Class Books
P. O. Box 1, Portishead
Bristol BS20 9 BR

Acknowledgments

To Les Storey

with sincere appreciation and thanks for his guidance and support.

Les Storey, RGN, CMS, Diploma in Management, Diploma in Management Training, is Vocational Development Manager, Lancashire College of Nursing and Health Studies.

Beverly Robertson, Editor

Kate Corkery Spencer, Editorial Assistant

Tom Bowman, Illustrations

First Class Books
P.O. Box 1, Portishead,
Bristol BS20 9BR
Telephone: (0823) 323 126
Fax: (0823) 321 876

Introduction

The Level 3 National Vocational Qualifications/Scottish Vocational Qualifications (NVQ/SVQ) in Care Award provides a set of performance standards for Care Support Workers from all occupational groups. The care standards specify the quality of performance in the workplace for those people who deliver hands-on care. Achieving the standards develops competence for assisting care professionals in institutional and community settings.

This workbook provides the enabling knowledge relating to the eight core units of the Level 3 award. The core units are the units of competence that are common to all NVQ/SVQ in Care Awards undertaken at Level 3.

- Promote equality for all individuals.

- Contribute to the protection of individuals from abuse.

- Contribute to the management of aggressive and abusive behaviour.

- Promote communications with clients where there are communication difficulties.

- Support clients when they are distressed.

- Enable clients to make use of available services and information.

- Contribute to the health, safety, and security of individuals and their environments.

- Obtain, transmit, and store information relating to delivery of care service.

The Level 3 NVQ/SVQ in Care Award is part of the framework of qualifications leading to the Diploma in Social Work and is an entry qualification for people who would like to undertake nurse training.

It is important to remember that Care Support Workers are under the direction and supervision of qualified professionals. These qualified practitioners must retain accountability for assessment, planning, and standards of care and for determining the activity of support staff. It is important that Care Support Workers should not be allowed to work beyond their level of competence (UKCC, 1992).

Contents

Module 1

Promoting Equality For All

Unit O

· the core, value base unit for all NVQ/SVQ Awards in Care

Unit O outlines the principles of good practice in interacting with other people. The competencies in this unit are an integral part of the other units and, therefore, have to be demonstrated within all of the other units.

Promote equal opportunities and rights for all.

Objectives:

☐ Recognise various forms of discrimination.

☐ Describe how equality can be promoted.

☐ Explain how stereotyping can lead to prejudice.

☐ Outline the effects of institutionalisation.

☐ Describe how confidentiality should be maintained.

☐ Explain human and legal rights.

☐ Describe how personal beliefs can affect the provision of care.

☐ Outline how to build good relationships.

☐ Describe the appropriate use of verbal and non-verbal skills in communication.

Module 1 Glossary

advocate	someone who speaks up on behalf of, and for the benefit of, another person	label	classifying word or phrase that identifies something
depersonal- isation	one effect on a person of an institutionalised environment in which there is little opportunity for individual expression, e.g., lack of personal possessions, no privacy	non-verbal communication	aspects of communication that are not spoken, often referred to as body language (facial expression, gestures, posture, eye contact, touch)
discrimination	perceived differences (usually showing a preference) between alternatives	prejudice	an unfavourable opinion formed without proper judgement
empathy	the ability to accurately perceive the feelings of another, and the ability to communicate that understanding to him or her	significant other	a relative, friend, or someone who is important to another person
		stereotype	refers to a set of characteristics which are held to be common to members of a category
halo effect	tendency to conform to others' expectations	stigma	unpleasant or disgraceful characteristics attached to a person or group of people
institutional- isation	the effect on a person who lives in an environment where there is rigidity of routine, block treatment, depersonalisation, and little opportunity to express individuality	verbal communication	refers to communicating by mouth (words, language, tone of voice)

Part 1	**Ensuring Anti-Discriminating Practice** *(O.a)*

Everyone deserves to be treated with respect and dignity.

Always provide quality care, regardless of a person's background, beliefs, race, ethnicity, gender, sexuality, age, mental, or physical ability. Your personal beliefs and preferences should not affect the quality of service you provide.

Your personal beliefs affect your behaviour in a variety of direct and indirect ways. As a care worker, you need to be aware of legislation and local organisational policies that prohibit discriminatory practice (unfair treatment).

If you have any feelings of hostility toward population groups, be careful not to express those feelings at work. Seek advice on how to deal with your feelings.

There are different types of discrimination. **Overt discrimination** operates when a person is openly discriminating (e.g., advertising that your club is only open to white-skinned people).

Covert discrimination is much more difficult to prove. An example is an organisation whose managers are all males, but the majority of employees are women.

Appropriate discrimination can take the form of refusing to employ convicted child abusers to work in a children's home, or not allowing children with epilepsy to play on the high-climbing frame.

Inappropriate (but not illegal) **discrimination** can take the form of employing only people under the age of 55 years into senior management posts. Another example is accepting unnecessary rude and aggressive behaviour from a disabled person, just because he or she is disabled.

Equal Opportunities

The Equal Opportunities Commission (1986) outlined 10 aspects that should be written into organisational policies if they are to become equal opportunity employers. The policies should include the following:

- definition of direct and indirect sex and marriage discrimination, victimisation, and sexual harassment

- statement of the organisation's commitment to equal opportunities

- name of the officer(s) responsible for ensuring the policy is carried out

- details for how the policy is to be carried out

- an obligation upon employees to respect and act in accordance with the policy

- procedures for dealing with complaints of discrimination

- examples of unlawful practices

- details of monitoring and reviewing procedures

- commitment to remove barriers to equal opportunity

- provision of equal opportunities training

Suggested reading:
- Sex Discrimination Act (Home Office, 1975)
- Race Relations Act (Home Office, 1976)
- Disabled Persons Act (DHSS, 1986)

Promote Equality

To promote equality, it is important to recognise and accept other people's beliefs and lifestyles (even when they clash with your own). Every individual has the right to equality and quality of life, regardless of the person's past history and beliefs. Seek advice if you are unsure of appropriate behaviour or if you have discriminatory feelings.

Protect yourself and others from discrimination by taking appropriate action:

- Provide feedback to anyone who has been discriminatory about the effects and consequences of his or her actions.

- Offer support and guidance to people who have been discriminated against and to those at-risk from discrimination.

- Make a formal complaint about any discrimination you encounter, or support others in doing so.

Exercise

Obtain a copy of equal opportunities policies for your organisation. After you read them, do the following exercises:

1. Evaluate whether the policies provide appropriate guidance to staff on anti-discriminatory behaviour.

2. Check how equal opportunities are promoted within your organisation, e.g., study days, brochures, etc.

3. Evaluate whether the employees of your organisation tend to behave in ways that are non-discriminatory.

Write your findings in the form of a report. Discuss the report with your manager or your NVQ/SVQ Assessor. Add your report and details of the discussion to your portfolio.

Stereotyping and Prejudice

All people take on roles or have roles given to them during their lives. Many roles have stereotypes attached to them on the basis that people from the same role groups have similar characteristics or traits (e.g., Scots are mean, redheads are fiery, accountants are boring, etc.). Therefore, people sometimes attribute a variety of qualities or labels to an individual that are radically wrong.

Some stereotypes have positive values attached to them and some have negative values attached, referred to as a stigma. A person with a stigma is often the target of discrimination.

In the care sector, there are several client groups that tend to carry a stigma, e.g., the elderly, the disabled, the mentally ill, and people who have learning disabilities. This stigma leads to the halo effect where there is a strong tendency for these people to conform to other people's negative expectations of them. People's negative expectations affect the quality of their interactions with stigmatised individuals, further reducing chances for improvement.

Institutionalisation

The effects of stigma are most easily seen when large groups of people receiving care become institutionalised. This occurs when care provision is not client-centred and is characterised by the following:

- **rigidity of routine**: where patterns of care vary little from day to day, e.g., bedtimes same at weekends as during the week

- **block treatment**: frequent occasions when clients are herded together, e.g., to the bathroom or toilets

- **depersonalisation**: little opportunity to express individuality, e.g., no privacy, few or no personal possessions

- **distance between staff and clients**: a sharp separation of roles, e.g., separate staff toilets, different cutlery

The effect of institutionalisation on clients is that they become dehumanised:

- loss of interest in things and events

- non-resentment of harsh or unfair treatment

- lack of interest in the future and inability to make plans

- lack of attention to personal hygiene and appearance

- becoming resigned to the fact that nothing will ever change

The emphasis of care for these groups of people is to get them out of the large institutions and into the community. In the community they can be encouraged to live their lives as normally as possible.

| Part 2 | **Maintaining Confidentiality** *(O.b)* |

Ensure right of access before disclosing personal details about anyone in your care.

Information about the people in your care is very private. Confidential information includes all medical information (diagnosis, prognosis, and treatment) and everything related to personal, social, and financial matters.

You have both a legal and moral responsibility to maintain confidentiality about personal information. Information is disclosed only to those who have the right and the need to know, according to statutory or agency policies. Never disclose information unless you have proof of the inquirer's identity and right of access.

The UKCC (1987) provides general guidelines on confidentiality, emphasizing accountability for confidential information obtained in the course of practice. Refrain from disclosing information without the consent of the client (or person entitled to act on his or her behalf). The only exceptions are when disclosure is required by law, or by the order of a court, or is necessary in the public interest.

Data Protection Act (1984) gives individuals the right of access to information held about them on computers. It is a criminal offence to disclose computer-based, personal data to third parties unless that person is registered as having a right of access to the information. Conflict can arise between confidentiality and the need to share information with other parties, (e.g., other care workers or the police). A section in the act allows personal data to be disclosed when it is essential for purposes of preventing or detecting a crime or for the apprehension or prosecution of offenders.

Access to Health Records Act (NHSME, 1990) enables everyone over 16 years of age the right to see their health records unless there are compelling reasons to deny access. A health record is defined as any record concerning the physical or mental health of an individual who can be identified from the information, e.g., details of investigations, diagnosis, treatment, or examinations (physical or mental).

Application for access to health records is made by writing to the holder of the records, (e.g., doctor or health authority). The application must be fully processed within 40 days, and a fee may be charged up to £10 plus the cost of postage and copying (unless the applicant simply reads the records on the spot).

It is important for care staff to take great care with health records:

· Record factually.

· Record honestly.

· Be non-judgemental and do not show prejudice.

· Inform clients that they can ask for incorrect or unsubstantiated information to be deleted, or they can insert statements that they disagree with the information.

All records with confidential information should be kept secure when not in use and should never be discussed in public. If you suspect abuse of confidential information, or if you have any concerns about confidentiality, seek advice.

Breaching Confidentiality

There may be times when you are told information that needs to be passed on to someone else for action (e.g., when someone is at-risk). Carefully explain to the person who told you that you may have to share the information with others (e.g., when you find out that a person has AIDS, is a drug abuser, or is contemplating suicide). Explain the reasons why the information should be shared with others and who, precisely, will have access to the information.

Confidentiality can be inadvertently breached when members of staff are not as careful as they should be with confidential information. This most often occurs in the following ways:

· talking about clients in corridors, on public transport, etc., where other people can hear

· leaving case notes lying around where unauthorised people can simply pick them up and read them

· leaving personal information unattended on computer screens for unauthorised people to read

If you see or hear breach of confidentiality, take action immediately:

· Lock case notes away.

· Blank out computer screens or turn the screen so that nobody unauthorised can see it.

· Courteously point out to the people concerned that they are breaching confidentiality, that they should refrain from doing so, and that their jobs are at-risk if they are caught or reported.

· If confidentiality is being blatantly breached, despite warnings, report the people concerned to an appropriate manager.

Part 3 Upholding Rights and Choices in Service Delivery *(O.c)*

Promote individual rights and encourage choices.

Promote and support the rights of each person in your care, and encourage everyone to express his or her needs and wishes. When individuals make choices, this encourages their independence.

- Stick to your promises and inform people if you are going to be late.

- Be specific in your options. Let people know if the options are reduced, explain why, and make a record of the transaction.

- If someone is unable to make choices, take the person's interests into account before making a choice for the person. Where possible, consult an advocate, friend, relative, or significant other.

- Give a clear explanation when a person's request cannot be granted or must be restricted.

- Do not allow yourself or others to be manipulated.

- If you have concerns about offering choices, seek advice.

Some client groups are much more likely to be deprived of their rights to available services because of the effects of prejudice and because they may not actively seek services (e.g., gypsies, tramps, New-Age travellers, some ethnic minorities). The emphasis with these groups must be to inform them of available services and ensuring access to those services.

Rights

The **Universal Declaration of Human Rights** (United Nations, 1948) had considerable impact throughout the world. The declaration includes the following rights:

- recognition as a person before the law

- education and employment

- self-determination

- life

- not being subjected to medical experimentation without consenting

- social security

- adequate standard of living, including food, clothing, and housing

The **Declaration of Rights of Mentally Retarded Persons** (United Nations, 1971) recognised that people with learning disabilities might not be adequately covered by the previous declaration. This declaration outlines that people with learning disabilities:

- should have the same rights as other people, insomuch as this is feasible

- should have a guardian (advocate) appointed if they cannot make their own decisions

The **Mental Health Act** (1983) addresses the following legal rights:

- voting

- entering hire purchase contracts

- entering into marriage

- having property and assets protected

- having protection against cruelty and exploitation

- writing to certain members of society

The "law of the land" gives citizens further rights. For example:

- to vote

- to demonstrate

- to legal representation

- to protection from theft and physical harm

Care in the Community

Guidelines were established by the Department of Health (1990) for Local Authorities to be responsible for planning the provision of community care services in their localities. Local Authorities work in conjunction with:

- district health authorities

- family health service authorities

- local housing authorities

- voluntary organisations

Services have been established so that, where possible, people who need care in the community have the right to the available services:

- domiciliary, day, and respite services to enable people to live in their own homes, where feasible and sensible

- a full assessment of needs and the delivery of a negotiated package of services to meet those needs

- practical support for families who provide care for relatives at home

Patient's Charter

The Patient's Charter (Department of Health, 1991) clearly sets out people's rights to care and standards of service. The charter has seven existing rights, three new rights, and nine standards.

Existing rights:

- to receive health care on the basis of clinical need, regardless of the ability to pay

- to be registered with a general practitioner

- to receive emergency medical care at any time

- to be referred to a consultant who is personally acceptable and to be referred for a second opinion

- to be given clear explanations of any proposed treatment, including any risks and alternatives, before agreeing to the treatment

- to have access to your own health records and for the contents to be kept confidential

- to choose whether or not to take part in medical research or medical student training

New rights:

- to be provided with detailed information on local health services, including quality standards and maximum waiting times

- to be guaranteed admission for treatment by a specific date, no later than two years from the date the person was placed on the waiting list

- to have any complaint about the National Health Service (NHS) investigated, and to receive a prompt and full written reply to the complaint

Standards:

- respect for privacy, dignity, and religious and cultural beliefs

- arrangements to ensure that everyone can use the services, including people with special needs

- provision of information to relatives and friends

- ambulance service to arrive at an emergency within 14-19 minutes

- immediate assessment in the Accident and Emergency Department

- being seen within 30 minutes of appointment time in the outpatient clinic

- operations not being cancelled on the day of the operation

- a named nurse or midwife responsible for each patient

- arrangements made before discharge from hospital to ensure appropriate care is provided at home

---

Exercise

People in your care are likely to be very vulnerable. Sit down and talk to two or three of them about their lifestyles. Assess whether they are receiving all their human and legal rights. If not, find out why.

Discuss your findings with a colleague or your NVQ/SVQ Assessor.

Part 4	**Respecting Personal Beliefs** *(O.d)*

Recognise and support individual beliefs and preferences.

Actively encourage people in your care to express their beliefs, wishes, and views, as long as they do not interfere with the rights of others. Personal beliefs and preferences are important. Acknowledge individual beliefs about self, race, religion, politics, culture, ethics, and sexuality. Respond in a manner that is supportive.

Also, be aware of your own beliefs if they are likely to cause conflict in the provision of care (e.g., if you are a strict Catholic, you will not want to be involved in abortions and family planning). Tell your supervisor if your care role conflicts with your religious or other beliefs.

Beliefs and preferences affect the foods people eat, the clothing they wear, how they worship, and many other aspects of daily living. You can support an individual's beliefs in a variety of ways.

- Be sensitive to each person's needs.

- Support the right to practice individual beliefs.

- Make sure your speech and actions do not offend others.

- Address individuals by their preferred names and titles.

- Take into consideration beliefs and lifestyles when planning care.

- Be respectful of each person's customs and possessions.

- Show interest in each person's beliefs.

- Be willing to listen when a person wants to talk.

- Never question or make fun of another person's beliefs.

- Never try to force your religious beliefs on another person.

- Never ask non-Christians for their ''Christian names.'' (Ask for their first names.)

Learn all you can about religions, customs, and beliefs, including practices of ethnic minorities in your local area. Ask people to tell you about their beliefs and traditions, or go to the local library for information.

Religious Customs

Be familiar with religious customs (e.g., Sikh men must leave their hair unshorn and wear a turban). The more you know, the less likely you are to accidentally offend someone. People may have religious items in their possession (such as rosaries or prayer books). If you must move these items, handle them with respect.

Holidays

Be aware of days that are celebrated with special rituals (e.g., Passover for Jews). People may need extra help dressing for holidays, or they may need privacy for certain rituals (such as confession or prayer).

Foods

Some religions forbid certain foods. Know what is not allowed and offer other choices. (For example, most Moslems and Hindus do not eat pork or beef; the only meat that Moslems eat is Halal meat that has been killed a special way). Be aware of special times that people may fast (go without food) or eat only certain foods (e.g., Ramadan for Moslems).

Clothing

Some religions have certain articles of clothing that must be worn or treated with respect (e.g., devout Moslem women may only leave their eyes uncovered in public).

Medical Treatments

Be aware of any medical treatments that are not allowed because of religious beliefs (e.g., blood transfusions for Jehovah's Witness followers).

Clergy

If an individual wants to see a member of clergy, make sure all relevant people are informed. Provide privacy whenever a member of clergy visits.

Death

Religions have different rules governing what to do with a body after death. (For example, followers of Islam should not be touched by non-Moslems after death, or if they have to be touched, you should wear gloves).

Exercise

If you care for a significant number of people from ethnic minorities, go to the library and find out more about their cultures and religions. Sit down and have a chat with some of these people to learn more about them .

Write up your findings and include them in your portfolio.

Part 5	**Establishing Effective Communication** *(O.e)*

Everything you do or say communicates a message.

Good relationships are the foundation for a comfortable working experience. Treating people with respect and dignity builds good relationships.

· **Always knock** before entering a person's room. Remember that this is an individual's living quarters. Provide the privacy and courtesy you would show to people in their own homes.

· **Introduce yourself.** Some people have difficulty remembering names. Say your name whenever you enter a person's room to avoid confusion or embarrassment.

· **Ask how a person wishes to be addressed.** Some elderly people prefer not to be called by their first names.

· **Provide comfort.** Pay attention to a person's needs.

· **Support individual rights and choices** within the limits of your work role. Encourage individuals to express their wishes and needs.

· **Be courteous and respectful of visitors.** Family and friends influence the well-being of individuals. Provide privacy, if desired. If you must provide care, politely ask visitors to leave the room and let them know when they can return.

· **Maintain privacy and dignity at all times.** Everyone wants to be loved and have friends with shared interests. Regardless of age, people are sexual beings with sexual desires. You must deal with sexuality in a mature, professional manner. Allow people plenty of privacy and do not interfere with consenting partners as long as the individuals concerned are not likely to come to any harm. If problems arise, ask your manager how to handle the situation.

Communication Skills

Communication is the giving and exchanging of information. At least two people are involved, a speaker and a listener. Effective communication involves both good speaking skills and good listening skills.

The ability to communicate well builds good working relationships with the people in your care and the care team. Effective communication occurs through a variety of methods, using language that is easily understood.

The way you speak and listen sends messages to anyone who is listening or observing. Communication can positively or adversely affect everything you do in your work role.

It is important that verbal and non-verbal communications agree in order to send clear messages. Problems arise because most people are not aware of their non-verbal behaviour. If a person's verbal and non-verbal communications do not agree, the listener gets a mixed message.

Unfortunately, when messages are mixed, the non-verbal communication is often perceived with more clarity by the listener. For example, if you try to express concern while looking in another direction, you communicate that you are not interested.

Verbal Communication

Use appropriate language when communicating with people in your care.

- Use an interpreter if you do not speak a common language. (Be aware of the impact that a third person may have on willingness to disclose and on confidentiality.)

- Communicate with people at their level of understanding. Use an appropriate manner, level, and pace, according to individual abilities.

- Speak slowly, repeating yourself where necessary.

- Modify your communication, if necessary, to get the message across.

- Do not shout at people who are having difficulty understanding you.

- Do not use medical jargon or other long words which may confuse people.

Non-Verbal Communication

Non-verbal communication is at least as important as the words you use in face-to-face interactions. Your non-verbal behaviour is of critical importance in the regulation of communication, e.g., encouraging others to speak, ensuring others to be silent when you speak, ending a conversation, etc.

Many messages are conveyed by non-verbal communication. By your non-verbal actions, people can interpret whether you are happy or sad, feelings of dominance or subordination, friendliness or anger.

Non-verbal behaviour varies from person-to-person and between cultures. Actions that are commonplace for some may be totally unacceptable to others.

- **Touch**: British people do not touch very much when communicating compared to the Continentals. The places of the body that you touch are bound by social rules. For example, guiding another person's movements by steering at the elbow is acceptable, but putting your hand on a man's or woman's knee or thigh while talking may be highly unacceptable.

- **Gaze**: interaction often starts with a gaze. The person listening gives more eye contact than the one talking. Too much eye contact or staring creates anxiety.

- **Hand movements:** are mainly used as illustrators and emphasisers. They can also replace speech, e.g., Makaton or sign language.

- **Facial expression:** is most closely observed during interaction as it modifies everything that is said or done by showing emotions, providing feedback, indicating attitude, etc.

- **Posture:** is also very important in communicating attitudes and feelings. For example, at the start of an informal interview, it is important to sit straight, facing the person, leaning slightly forward to indicate interest. Talk to people at the same physical level, if possible. Do not stand over them as this can be intimidating.

- **Distance:** often indicates the relationship between two people. Spouses, lovers and children are usually allowed within 18 inches, the "intimate" space. From 18 inches to four feet is "personal" space for friends, and from four to nine feet is "social" space for most relationships. However, personal space varies, and what invades the personal space of one person will not do so for another.

Barriers to Communication

Avoid the following barriers to communication:
- appearing bored or impatient
- threatening or using harsh language
- negating or devaluing a person
- jumping to conclusions
- passing judgement or giving unwanted advice
- arguing or interrupting
- distracting (e.g., fiddling or doodling)
- confusing people with multiple questions
- mumbling or confused presentation
- having physical barriers between you and the person (e.g., a desk).
- being in environments that are distracting or uncomfortable

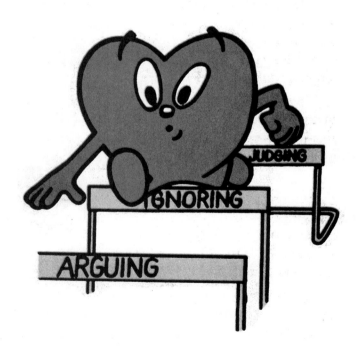

Exercise

Identify a person with whom it is difficult for you to talk. When you talk to this person, try to determine what this person does that makes communication difficult. If necessary, observe when the person talks with other people.

Check your findings by asking a colleague if he or she feels the same way when talking to the person.

Check Your Knowledge and Understanding

1. A young mother attends a clinic for counselling with her six-month-old son. You notice that the child has a number of linear bruises to his lower back and buttocks. The mother says the bruises are a result of falls. You know the woman and suspect that the child is being abused by her common-law husband. What would you do?

   a) Immediately inform the woman that you think the child has been beaten and that you are going to inform the Child Protection Officer.

   b) Inform the person in charge of the clinic about the situation.

   c) Decide to forget what you have seen on the grounds of confidentiality.

   d) Wait until you have finished work and make an anonymous phone call to the Child Protection Officer.

2. A person who has been a patient on your ward turns up one day. He confides that he is going to take the surgeon to court for botching his operation. He asks you to supply him with a copy of his computerised records so that they can be used as evidence in court. What would you do?

   a) Simply print a copy of the person's medical record and give it to him.

   b) Refuse to supply him with a copy of his medical records on the grounds that patients are not allowed to see their records.

   c) Inform the nurse-in-charge of the situation, and let the nurse deal with it.

   d) Contact the surgeon concerned so that he or she can come down to the ward to deal with this person's request.

3. Your boss, a married man, has started sexually harassing you by making occasional lewd suggestions and telling filthy jokes. You have politely asked him to stop, but he simply replied that he was only joking and walked away. The harassment has continued. What would you do?

    a) Slap his face the next time he sexually harasses you.

    b) Ask for a transfer or look for another job.

    c) Ignore your manager in the hope that he will stop harassing you.

    d) Report your manager's behaviour to the Personnel Department.

4. Which of the following is not a characteristic of institutionalised care?

    a) block treatment

    b) depersonalisation

    c) dehumanisation

    d) rigidity of routine

5. There are times when it is appropriate to breach confidentiality. Under which of the following situations would a breach of confidentiality be appropriate:

    a) A client informs you that she is contemplating suicide.

    b) A client informs you that he has been sexually abusing his step-daughter.

    c) A good friend of a patient who has been admitted to a psychiatric unit demands to know why her friend has been admitted.

    d) An insurance company rings you to ask about the diagnosis of a patient who has recently taken out a large life insurance policy.

6. A Moslem man is admitted to your residential home. He was recently discharged from hospital after treatment for a stomach complaint where he lost a lot of weight. He needs a healthy diet, but it is Ramadan and he refuses to eat between sunrise and sunset. What would you do?

    a) Insist that he eats his special diet at the same time as the other residents.

    b) Accept his fasting, offering him a slice of toast and a cup of tea for his supper.

    c) Allow his family to leave food for you to warm up for him at the times when he is allowed to eat.

    d) Insist that he goes home if he is not willing to follow the routines of the residential home.

See page 121 for answers.

19

Tips On Evidence Collection

1. If problems occur within your organisation related to discrimination, confidentiality, or rights and choices in service delivery, make notes on how they were handled and add them to your portfolio.

2. Make copies of any relevant organisational policies concerned with equal opportunities and confidentiality, and keep them in your portfolio.

3. If you get the chance to attend an equal opportunities or a communication skills workshop, keep a record of what you learned in your portfolio.

Module 1 References

Equal Opportunities Commission (1986) **Guidelines for Equal Opportunities Employers**. EOC: London.

Department of Health and Social Security (1983) **Mental Health Act**. HMSO: London.

Department of Health and Social Security (1986) **Disabled Persons Act**. HMSO: London.

Home Office (1975) **Sex Discrimination Act**. HMSO: London

Home Office (1976) **Race Relations Act**. HMSO: London.

Kagan C et al (1986) **A Manual of Interpersonal Skills for Nurses: An Experiential Approach**. Harper & Row: London.

United Kingdom Central Council for Nursing, Midwifery and Health Visiting (1987) **Confidentiality: An Elaboration of Clause 9**. UKCC: London.

United Nations (1948) **Universal Declaration of Human Rights**. UN: Geneva.

United Nations (1971) **Declaration on the Rights of Mentally Retarded Persons**. UN: Geneva.

Module 2

Protecting Individuals From Abuse

Unit Z1

- a core unit for both the Level 2 and Level 3 NVQ/SVQ Awards in Care

Unit Z1 is primarily concerned with minimising the level of abuse within care environments, minimising the effects of challenging behaviour, and monitoring individuals who may be at-risk from abuse.

Everyone should be protected from abuse.

Objectives:

- ☐ Identify causes of challenging behaviour.
- ☐ Describe the different types of abuse.
- ☐ Explain signs and symptoms of abuse.
- ☐ Describe a model for analysing challenging behaviour.
- ☐ Outline how to care for people at-risk.

Module 2 Glossary

abuse	mental, physical, sexual, medical, or financial abuse, exploitation or neglect
assault	an unlawful personal attack
assertiveness	ability to express views in a clear, confident, and direct manner, without denying the rights of others
battery	an attack where an actual blow is delivered
challenging behaviour	problem behaviour that is demanding and disruptive which makes it difficult to provide quality support and care
defamation	falsehoods (libel or slander) that result in damage to a person's reputation or character
false documentation	entries in a personal record that are not true
libel	a written, defamatory statement

negligence	failure to give assigned care, or giving improper care that causes harm (such as failure to raise bedrails resulting in someone falling out of bed)

non-compliance	refusal to do what one has been asked to do
paranoia	delusions (false perceptions) of persecution
slander	a spoken, defamatory statement

Part 1 Minimising Abuse in Care Environments (Z1.a)

You can contribute to minimising the level of abuse.

It is important to understand that there is always a reason for a person's behaviour. People receiving care are often adjusting to changes in their lifestyles that affect them physically, emotionally, and socially.

Individuals cope with their frustrations in different ways. Some people take out their anger on everyone; others may be quiet and withdrawn. Some people blame all of their problems on others; others blame themselves. Some deny there is a problem; others try to find a reason for everything.

Never express anger or irritation toward people in your care. Your attitude affects their behaviour and well-being. Understanding and accepting your own feelings is important. Whenever you feel frustrated, try to understand why you feel that way. If you are unable to cope with your feelings, seek advice.

Challenging Behaviour

Sometimes people are uncooperative, demanding, threatening, rude, or stubborn. Try to find the underlying cause of the behaviour. Some common concerns that affect people's behaviour:

- anxiety
- loneliness
- health problems
- pain
- change in lifestyle
- loss of independence
- unmet expectations
- fear
- grief
- financial concerns
- longing for the "old days"
- lack of understanding
- unmet needs
- religious concerns
- family problems
- depression
- lack of self-esteem
- physical and mental changes
- lack of sleep or rest

Occasionally, people become angry or upset about the situation of their loved one. Even though it may be difficult for you, try to be understanding and supportive of these people.

Abuse in the form of discrimination can occur if people are labelled as "difficult" or "awkward." Sometimes carers try to avoid these people, and this can make them more abusive.

Exercise

The behaviours of others can be an important factor in aggressive encounters. Spend a few minutes listing some of the things that make you angry. Ask some of your friends or colleagues to make a similar list. Group everybody's responses together, and you will find a long and varied list of potential irritants.

This exercise focuses your attention on the many and varied things that can upset people. Be aware that timing and mood are important variables which can make people react differently to the same stimulus at different times. For example, a person might be happy to listen to a long-winded joke most of the time, but it might make the person quite angry if you try telling the joke when he or she is rushing to make an appointment or when feeling ill.

Be aware of other factors that can cause challenging behaviour. Examples include:

- the influence of alcohol or drugs (prescribed or illegal)
- mental illness, especially when there are feelings of paranoia
- the environment (e.g., noisy, dirty, crowded, hot).
- having to wait and/or queue for long lengths of time
- your dress and professional manner, (representing unacceptable "authority")
- your irritating behaviour (e.g., showing boredom, interrupting other people's conversations)

23

Challenging behaviour can often be reduced by following these guidelines:

- offering advice and support, as appropriate, to help people understand why their inappropriate behaviour may be seen as abusive

- encouraging compromise solutions to conflict

- using interpersonal skills to deflect energies into useful activity rather than escalating conflict

Abuse

Abuse refers to any situation where a person's human or legal rights are refused, restricted, or curtailed.

People who are close to a person being abused often do not know and will not allow themselves to believe that it is happening. They may become very upset about the suspicions of care staff.

Abuse can take many forms and be short-term or long-term. It can be difficult to identify. For example, when does corporal punishment of a child become physical abuse, and when does a husband's bad temper become psychological abuse?

Abuse can be categorised according to the abuser:

- **self-abuse** (e.g., taking illegal drugs, purposeful self-injury)

- **other-abuse** (e.g., child abuse, granny bashing)

Abuse can also be categorised according to the nature of the abuse that has taken place:

- **physical abuse** (e.g., physical injuries from an attack or injuries caused by lack of an awareness of danger)

- **sexual abuse** (e.g., rape, indecent assault, allowing a child to watch blue movies)

- **psychological abuse** (e.g., creating anxiety over a period of time by the use of threats, not allowing a person to meet other people, institutionalisation)

Signs and Symptoms of Abuse

It is possible for the signs and symptoms detailed below to occur when there has been no abuse. Suspicion usually occurs when several of the signs and symptoms are noticed at once or over time. This may be linked to explanations that are inconsistent with the injury or behaviour.

Many of the short-term effects of abuse are well-documented. However, long-term effects can be more traumatic, especially if the victim exhibits behaviour that makes other people reject him or her.

Physical signs and symptoms:

- multiple bruises/bruises of different ages

- bruises on the face, especially around the mouth and ears

- splits on the inside of lips

- fingertip bruising (from having been forcibly gripped)

- bite marks (usually an oval bruise with a gap at each side)

- odd-shaped bruises that outline the shape of the weapon used

- scratch marks and bruises in difficult-to-injure places (e.g., inner thigh; inner or upper arm)

- burns and scalds (cigarette burns cause a round mark or scar one to one-and-one-half centimetres across)

- injuries and infections of the genitals

- general signs of neglect (including poor standards of hygiene and general nutrition)

- Munchausen syndrome by proxy (where the parent deliberately lies about a child's symptoms in order to obtain surgery for the child)

Psychological signs and symptoms:

- withdrawal and depression (avoiding eye contact, passivity, no spontaneous smiles)

- inappropriate/unacceptable behaviour (avoidance or attention-seeking behaviour, tantrums, aggression)

- anxiety (jumpy and tense, "frightened eyes")

- impaired capacity to enjoy life

- symptoms of psychiatric illness

Whether a person is abused in an isolated incident or over a prolonged period of time by one or many people, it is impossible to forecast what the long-term effects will be.

Managing Abuse

Whenever serious abuse is suspected, a person can be admitted to hospital or taken to a place of safety for observation for a more comprehensive assessment.

The most important aspects of caring for people who have been abused include:

- recognising the signs and symptoms of abuse

- making accurate records of what you observe or what is reported by the client

- informing an appropriate person of any concerns that you may have

- ensuring that you know the plan of care for the abused person (may include monitoring of the person's whereabouts, or placing restrictions on the person's movements, or restrictions on access to the person by potential visitors)

- offering advice to the person on how to avoid or minimise the level of abuse

---

Part 2 Handling Disruptive and Abusive Behaviour (Z1.b)

Try to minimise the negative effects of challenging behaviour.

It is essential to understand the cause of challenging behaviour before anything can be done to prevent or manage it (Poyner & Warne, 1988).

The Model for Understanding Challenging Behaviour allows for an analysis to be made of all incidents of challenging behaviour. The model consists of a carer interacting with a care recipient in a care environment to produce an outcome (challenging behaviour).

Model for Understanding Challenging Behaviour

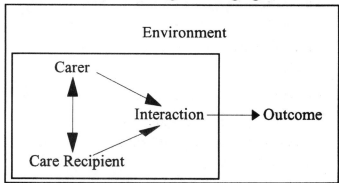

The Carer

Characteristics of the carer can have a significant effect on the outcomes of care provision.

- **Appearance** and first impressions are important in any job involving encounters with the public. For example, a uniform can prevent some people from being abusive but may stimulate others to be abusive.

- **Tolerance to stress** may be important for your success in dealing with difficult interactions. For example, your ability to control a group of boisterous children might be impaired if you are stressed by illness or work overload.

- **Experienced staff** have usually experienced similar situations before, and the expectation is that they are more likely to handle challenging behaviour effectively.

- **Gender** inevitably has an influence on challenging behaviour. For example, a woman might find it easier than a man to calm down an angry man, although women tend to feel more vulnerable to attack in certain situations.

- **Personality and temperament** of the carer affect behaviour. There are some care roles that automatically bring carers into contact with people who are likely to exhibit challenging behaviour (e.g., acute psychiatric units, welfare benefit offices).

- **Attitude** toward people who need care and their families and attitude to the job role tend to have an effect on how a carer behaves toward the people receiving care.

- **Expectations** that carers have about their jobs influence their ability to handle difficult situations. For example, a carer who always expects people to conform to the plan of care is likely to cause anger and resentment in people who do not agree with their planned care.

The Care Recipient

Characteristics of the care recipient can also have a significant effect on the outcomes of care provision.

- **Personality and temperament** of the care recipient affect behaviour. Some carers appear to be naturally better at handling difficult situations, usually because they have good interpersonal skills.

- **Temporary conditions** affect care, such as care recipients who are under the influence of drugs or alcohol or who are suffering from an illness or distress.

- **Negative or uncertain expectations** of the interaction to come can affect the situation. For example, a daughter expects that her father cannot be provided with the care he needs, and she is deeply concerned that he cannot remain in his own home.

- **Immaturity** can be a problem; children cannot be expected to control their emotions and behaviour.

Environment

Environment is the total context in which the service is delivered. Each environment has factors which have an effect on incidents of challenging behaviour. Care workers need to consider the following factors:

- **Working alone**: Home visits by health and social services staff are more difficult because the carers are guests in people's homes, and there is no back-up if events start to go wrong.

- **Job location**: Locally-based services are usually better able to respond sympathetically to difficult situations because they are aware of local issues. A person who provides services in a very rough area of town is more likely to encounter aggressive behaviour.

- **Cash or drugs being carried:** Carers are potential targets for robbers.

- **Waiting and queuing:** Some people do not cope well with waiting and may become irritable or agitated.

- **Time:** Consider the time of day. For example, people are more likely to be drunk at certain times of the day, and children are more likely to be on the streets at certain times of the day/week.

- **Territory**: People feel more comfortable on their own territory. Being uncomfortable can affect behaviour.

- **Room design:** This includes room temperature, available space, seating arrangements, decorations, furniture, etc. For example, high room temperatures are likely to make people drowsy, irritable, and aggressive.

Interaction

If a person receiving care believes that he or she is being treated in an unfair or unreasonable way, it is not unusual for challenging behaviour to occur. Outcomes of challenging behaviour can include a wide range of difficult-to-handle behaviours ranging from non-compliance and verbal abuse to spitting and physical assault.

When challenging behaviour occurs, be careful to keep your own feelings under control. Do not lose your temper, and try not to show fear or irritation.

If you are monitoring and recording a person's behaviour, try not to make it obvious, or you may get inaccurate results, and/or you may make matters worse. Make accurate and complete records of all incidents of challenging behaviour.

Responsibilities

Understand your employer's policies regarding handling aggression and violence. It is the employer's duty under the Health and Safety at Work Act (Department of Health, 1974) to ensure that the work environment is as safe as possible for employees. Examples include visible security systems for buildings where appropriate, adequate staffing, and appropriate training to handle aggression and violence. (Health and Safety Commission, 1987).

Exercise

Think back to an incident of challenging behaviour that you remember well. Make a note of the significant details concerning the incident, and write them down under the following five headings:

- carer
- care recipient
- environment
- interaction
- outcomes

Assess details of the incident, and comment on the following:

- Could/should the incident have been avoided?
- Could/should the incident have been handled better?

Discuss your analysis of the incident with your NVQ/SVQ Assessor and/or your manager, and ask for feedback on your assessment of the incident.

| Part 3 | **Monitoring Individuals Who Are At-Risk** *(Z1.c)* |

Report all complaints and any suspected abuse.

It is your legal responsibility to respect people's rights and to protect them from harm (such as assault, battery, defamation, false documentation, negligence, etc.). Legal action may result from abuse or failure to report suspected abuse.

If a person in your care has a complaint, or if you suspect abuse, report your evidence immediately to the person in charge. Make a detailed written record in your own handwriting while details are still fresh in your memory. The handwritten record should be retained (even if the report is eventually typed), as it can be used as evidence in court.

If a person in your care needs protection from abuse, be sure that you know the care plan and any rules or regulations that pertain to the situation. This includes ensuring that you know of any people in your care who are at-risk.

Caring For People At-Risk

Ensure that the care plan explicitly states the level of supervision or observation needed for anyone who is at-risk. Some care plans have a necessary and appropriate element of risk which has been agreed by the care team. (For example, allowing a person to travel to the day centre without supervision when there is a slight risk that he/she might get lost). Report any significant changes in the person's physical or mental condition immediately.

Report any signs or symptoms of abuse immediately. Sometimes it is important to point out the potential consequences of legal action that can be taken against a (potential) abuser.

Understand all legal and organisational policies and referral systems concerned with the types of abuse from which your client group are at-risk. Often there are other care agencies involved when there are people at-risk. Because of the implications of potential legal action, it is essential that the various agencies keep accurate records and communicate with each other.

There may be times when you learn that someone (who may or may not be a client) is at-risk. Carefully explain to the person who told you that you may have to share the information with others. Where possible, the information should be checked for accuracy.

If you have any concerns about dealing with abuse at work, seek advice.

Exercise

Answer the following questions about your area of work.

1. Have any of the people in your care been abused in the past? If the answer is yes, could/should it have been prevented? What action was taken?

2. Are any of them, currently, at-risk from abuse? If the answer is yes, how is this situation being managed in the plan of care? In your opinion, is the plan of care appropriate?

Write a report of your findings for inclusion in your portfolio and discuss it with your NVQ/SVQ Assessor.

Check Your Knowledge and Understanding

1. Which of the following are potential causes of challenging behaviour?

   a) anxiety

   b) having to wait

   c) lack of sleep or rest

   d) grief

2. Which of the following strategies is usually not appropriate for dealing with challenging behaviour?

   a) getting conflicting parties to negotiate a settlement

   b) reprimanding a person for being abusive or aggressive

   c) getting the conflicting parties to start work

   d) providing feedback to people about the effects of their challenging behaviour on others

3. Which of the following is not a sign of physical abuse?

   a) oval bruise with gaps at either side

   b) headache

   c) striped weals on the buttocks and lower back

   d) anxiety

4. Which of the following is not part of the model for analysing challenging behaviour?

   a) environment

   b) care recipient

   c) carer

   d) significant others

5. One of the people in your care makes a complaint that a fellow resident is continually threatening him with violence. What would you do?

   a) Make an immediate written record of the complaint.

   b) Write up the complaint in the care record at the end of the shift.

   c) Ignore the complaint in the hope that the situation will cool down over the next couple of days.

   d) Mention the problem to the person-in-charge, when she arrives on duty in four hours.

6. Which of the following strategies is not appropriate for a person who is at slight risk of minor physical abuse.

   a) Report signs and symptoms of abuse immediately to the person in charge.

   b) Ensure that the care plan outlines in detail the level of supervision that is required.

   c) Keep the person under constant supervision until there is no longer a risk.

   d) Report any significant changes in the person's physical or mental condition.

See page 121 for answers.

Tips On Evidence Collection

1. Make copies of any relevant organisational policies concerned with abuse in your field of work, and keep them in your portfolio.

2. If you attend a workshop on client abuse or handling challenging behaviour, keep the details in your portfolio.

Module 2 References

Department of Employment (1974) **Health and Safety at Work Act**. HMSO: London.

Health and Safety Commission (1987) **Violence To Staff In The Health Services**. HMSO: London.

Poyner B. and Warne C. (1988) **Health and Safety Executive Report: Preventing Violence to Staff**. HMSO: London.

Module 3

Unit Z3

· a core unit of the Level 3
NVQ/SVQ Award in Care

**Unit Z3 is primarily concerned
with the promotion of non-
aggressive and non-abusive
behaviour and the management
of aggressive incidents.**

Managing Aggressive and Abusive Behaviour

*Contribute to the active management of
aggressive and abusive behaviour.*

Objectives:

☐ Discuss personal behaviour that can provoke
aggression.

☐ Outline strategies to prevent aggression.

☐ Identify safety factors for home visiting.

☐ Outline assertion techniques for handling aggression.

☐ Describe tactics that can be used when faced with
violence.

☐ Outline appropriate methods of control and restraint.

☐ Describe simple break-away techniques.

☐ Describe the reporting of aggressive incidents.

☐ Explain legal issues concerned with handling
aggression.

Module 3 Glossary

break-away	techniques that allow a person to escape the grip of a violent attacker	self-disclosure	divulging personal information to another person
control and restraint	techniques that use minimum force as a last resort for handling extremely aggressive behaviour	violence	the application of force, severe threat, or serious abuse; severe verbal abuse or threat that is likely to turn into violence, serious or persistent harassment, threat with a weapon, major or minor injury
de-escalation	tactics that aim to calm an aggressor		

Part 1   Promoting Non-Aggressive/Non-Abusive Behaviour *(Z3.a)*

Where possible, prevent aggressive and abusive behaviour.

There has been increasing concern in recent years about the level of violence exhibited by recipients of care. One theory (Dingwall, 1984) suggests that increased violence is related to more women care workers being in positions of authority. Women with power to grant or deny care services sometimes cause resentment in a sexist society.

Today's faster pace of life and social problems result in more people suffering from the effects of stress. Aggression is often a natural behavioural response to irritation. Everyone has times when they are unable to suppress feelings of anger. Sometimes those feelings lead to outbursts of aggression. The way people judge the appropriateness of an aggressive outburst tends to highlight discrimination. For example, men are expected to be more aggressive than women, and people from hot countries are generally supposed to have hotter tempers.

People have become knowledgeable about care services and their rights. Not everyone's expectations can be met, which has led to a general increase in abuse and aggression toward care workers.

To manage aggression, the emphasis must be on prevention and de-escalation before violence occurs. Most interpersonal aggression aimed at care staff is caused by an action, or a failure to carry out an action, by a member of care staff.

Avoid personal behaviour which can provoke or escalate aggression:

· Avoid using a tone of voice that is nagging, demanding, or showing boredom.

· Do not break off conversations without apologising, and always try to return to a conversation after an interruption.

- Do not overreact by using abusive language or issuing threats.

- Avoid getting into arguments.

- Do not ignore questions or the people posing the questions.

- Try to remain calm. Although abuse is personal in nature, do not take it personally.

- Accept apologies gracefully.

- Do not use phrases such as "Calm down" or "Don't be silly." These "talk down" to the person and belittle the problem.

- Avoid laughing, chatting, reading magazines, etc., in front of people who are waiting.

- Use appropriate non-verbal communication. Do not shrug shoulders, raise eyebrows, point, commence clock watching, stand with hands on hips or arms folded across the chest, etc.

- Do not point at, or push, an aggressor.

- If possible, keep your hands below waist level, and keep them out of your pockets.

- Maintain a normal distance between yourself and the aggressor.

- Try to get the aggressor to sit down and talk.

Strategies to Prevent Aggressive Behaviour

Treat people with respect and dignity. Nothing is likely to irritate another person more than being "spoken down to." Try to appear confident but concerned. Avoid pat responses, e.g., "Everything will be alright." Evaluate your own performance during your interactions with people who are being abusive.

Maintain personal control of your feelings. Remain calm, regardless of the situation. Showing your anger or displeasure is likely to escalate the conflict.

Be honest with people. Although it is important to control your own anger, sometimes it is necessary to reveal your personal feelings. Communicate openly and effectively, to promote acceptance and trust.

Provide face-saving alternatives. Be willing to bargain and compromise by providing alternatives from which a person can choose. This promotes a willingness to accept the care being provided. For example, a person complaining about the timing of meals could be offered alternative eating arrangements.

Set limits to behaviour. Communicate clear messages about what is expected. Be consistently firm, and be assertive where necessary, (e.g., asking a person to stop smoking in a room that is clearly marked with "no smoking" signs).

Promote expression of feelings. Allow and acknowledge feelings of anger or fear, and encourage the safe expression of those feelings. When appropriate, allowing a person the chance to "let off steam" may prevent the problem from escalating to violence.

Monitor people's behaviour. The care provider continually assesses the environment so that he or she can choose the right moment and right manner to intervene. Monitoring involves recognising patterns of behaviour and getting to know the people who are receiving care. Especially important is being sensitive to non-verbal behaviours exhibited by both yourself and others.

Provide time to calm down. People need time to calm down or to talk through the problem. Getting the person to describe the problem helps to refocus thinking on the problem rather than on acting out the anger. Talking often provides the essential cooling down period.

Exercise

Think of the person who most irritates you. Write down the things that this person does that irritate you.

Identify the person's irritating characteristics or behaviours. Then check which of the previously mentioned "strategies to prevent aggressive behaviour" the person is not using.

Assertion

Assertiveness refers to a person's ability to express his or her views in a clear, confident, and direct manner without denying the rights of others. Assertive behaviour is always preferable to passive or aggressive behaviour.

Your clear, confident, and direct manner means that you can resolve problems without resorting to threats or manipulation. It also allows you to calmly handle criticism and uncertainty. Assertion can help people to refuse requests without feeling guilty, or to ask for help when it is needed without feeling inadequate.

Handling Abusive/Aggressive Behaviour

The following assertion techniques can be used as a means of handling abusive and aggressive behaviour (Wondrak, 1989):

1. **Self-disclosure**: admitting to an aggressor that you are afraid.

2. **Partial agreement**: agreeing with part of a person's criticism. (E.g., ''Yes, I could have handled the situation a little better, but I am happy with the way things have turned out.'')

3. **Gentle confrontation**: confronting a person in an attempt to uncover the reason for the abusive behaviour. (E.g., ''I am sorry, I did not mean to upset you by opening all the upstairs windows. What is the problem?'')

4. **Side-stepping**: agreeing fully with a person's criticism. (E.g., ''Yes, it was silly to close all the windows when it is so hot.'')

5. **Being specific**: keeping what you have to say as specific as possible and avoiding unnecessary waffle. (E.g., ''John, I notice you keep kicking Jane under the table.'')

Checklist for Making Home Visits
(DHSS, 1988)

Have you:

- received relevant training concerning violence to staff?

- developed a sound grasp of your unit's safety policy for visitors?

- developed a clear idea about the area into which you are going?

- carefully previewed today's cases and checked whether anybody who is in your care is potentially violent?

- asked to have a colleague present, taken an escort, or used a taxi, if unsure?

- made appointment(s)?

- left your itinerary with expected departure/ arrival times?

- told colleagues, manager, etc., about possible changes to the plan?

- arranged for contact if your return is overdue?

Do you carry:

- forms to report and record incidents?

- a personal alarm or portable telephone? Does it work? Is it handy?

- a bag/briefcase, wear an outer uniform, or have car stickers that suggest you have money or drugs with you? Is this wise where you are going today/tonight?

- an out-of-hours telephone number that can be used to summon help?

Can you:

- be certain your attitude, body language, etc., will not cause trouble?

- defuse potential problems and manage aggression?

Remember the three Vs of visiting:

VET

VERIFY

VIGILANCE

Part 2   Managing Outbursts of Aggression *(Z3.b)*

Control your temper during outbursts of aggression and abusive behaviour.

When challenging behaviour occurs, try to defuse the situation so that dangers and disturbances to others are kept to a minimum. If you require assistance, get help immediately and do not forget to provide care to the victim of the violent attack.

If a person in your care exhibits aggressive behaviour, follow the plan of care for the person, including any rules or regulations pertaining to the situation. Channel your own emotions and energies into dealing with the situation. Never lose your temper.

Guidelines If Violence Occurs

(Farrell & Gray, 1992)

- **Breathing**: Breathe deeply, rhythmically, and deliberately.

- **Posture**: Relax and balance your weight evenly for effective and rapid movement.

- **Thought patterns**: Think realistically and optimistically about your situation.

- **Emotional control**: Accept feelings of panic, anger, and fear as normal. Control these feelings by concentrating on your breathing, posture, and thought control.

- **Behavioural control**: Do not be discouraged if you make a mistake in a crisis. Concentrate on behaving in ways that will make the situation less dangerous.

Other Tactics

- **Getting help**: Explain that you need to let your office know where you are so that you can be contacted. Or say that you need to let your colleagues know where you are so that you will not be disturbed. This may allow you to give a coded message for help.

- **Escaping**: Listen carefully to what the person has to say while considering escape options if the situation gets out of control.

- **Diverting attention**: Divert the person's attention from violence by talking about something that interests the person.

Your Legal Position

It is an offence to ill-treat or wilfully neglect a person in your care. The use of force is illegal except where the law permits it, e.g., self-defence.

The use of compulsory medical treatment is very limited, e.g., people detained under appropriate sections of the Mental Health Act (1983).

If you act ''in good faith,'' you are protected as long as your actions are deemed reasonable. For example, you might accidentally injure a person while protecting yourself from attack. Or you might need to use reasonable force if someone is behaving in ways that are dangerous to himself or others.

You also have a legal right to ask somebody to leave the premises or to have the person removed if he or she refuses to leave. The person who refuses to leave when requested is deemed to be a trespasser. Repeatedly and courteously ask the person to leave. If the person refuses to leave, call the police.

Control and Restraint

Control and restraint techniques do not offer any magic solutions and are not intended as a form of unarmed combat. They are a tactic of last resort. All other means of controlling or defusing the situation should be tried first.

Restraint may be necessary for the following reasons (Department of Health, 1990):

- physical assault

- destructive behaviour

- non-compliance with treatment

- self-harm or risk of physical injury by accident

- overactivity likely to result in exhaustion

It is impossible to prescribe when restraint should be used. The advantages and disadvantages of intervening have to be assessed. For example, it may be preferable to have a couple of chairs smashed or a window broken, rather than risk injury to yourself and others by intervening. But, if it looks as though a lot of furniture is going to be smashed or that people are in danger of being hurt, you must intervene.

Restraining people requires attention to detail to ensure that the best possible outcomes are achieved. Remember that the person who is being aggressive has a right to the best care possible. You should not be expected to restrain a person on your own because you put both yourself and the other person at an increased risk of being injured.

It may be the policy in your organisation that care staff do not restrain. This may be left to security staff or the police. Ensure that you know your organisation's policies for handling aggression and violence.

A recent report (Department of Health, 1992) recommended that control and restraint should be avoided whenever possible. Restraining equipment and seclusion should no longer be used.

Before Restraint

Identify one person who is to take charge of the exercise, coordinate actions, and try to calm the aggressive person by talking to him or her.

Assess the situation while help is gathering. Check that the environment is safe for restraint. Check for furniture and objects that could become potential weapons or could get damaged in the process, and move them out of the way. Onlookers should be shepherded away, if possible.

Assemble enough staff to carry out the restraint. Preferably, there should not be fewer than five staff, excluding anyone who is going to administer medication. Keep trying to talk to the person during this stage, explaining the consequences of his/her actions. A show of strength may be enough to defuse the situation.

Establish the aim of restraint. This will usually be obvious. For example:

- to provide treatment compulsorily (this should be established beforehand to ensure the treatment is lawful, e.g., the 1983 Mental Health Act)
- to restrain a person until he calms down and stops being a danger to himself and others

- to stop a child from trying to escape who is detained under the Children and Young Persons Act (1933)

Prepare yourself for physical contact by removing dangerous items from your person, e.g., watches, combs, pens, etc.

During Restraint:

Be committed to the restraint; half-hearted attempts may put yourself and others at-risk of injury.

Apply force safely during the restraint. Using five members of staff enables one to restrain each limb when the person is on the floor, while the fifth takes responsibility for the head.

The person at the head keeps talking, trying to calm the person and assess when it is safe to discontinue the restraint. Occasionally, the person's hair may have to be firmly grasped to prevent biting. Care must be taken to ensure that pressure is not placed on the throat of the person being restrained.

The other members of staff hold the limbs by lying with their weight over the major joints to minimise their lever effect, taking care not to twist or bend limbs or joints or to cause unnecessary injury.

Any form of restraint should be time-limited and should last for the minimum possible period of time. Make provision for care after restraint, e.g., arrange to counsel the person. While waiting for the person to calm down, the option of administering medication to the person can be considered.

It is possible, in some circumstances, to apply a lesser form of restraint than outlined. For example, a very confused long-term resident might insist on "going home," refusing all requests to return to the residential home. In this case, two people may be enough to restrain him with dignity and return him to safety.

Two members of staff, facing the same way as the resident, move to either side of the resident. Each places the nearest arm under and around the resident's upper arm, leaving the outside hand to hold his wrist and gently guide him back to the residential home.

Break-away

Break-away techniques allow you to break free and permit an escape from an aggressor who has a grip on you when there is nobody readily available to help you. Break-away techniques should be practiced under supervision in a recognised course before attempting to use them. Otherwise, the techniques might prove to be unsuccessful, unnecessary, or cause injury. Knowing break-away techniques instils self-confidence in staff who face aggression in their work.

Your interpersonal skills will not always prevent you from being attacked. The primary aim of break-away techniques is to produce sharp pain and/or cause surprise in your attacker. The intent is to allow you to escape to safety and/or allow time for help to arrive. Hopefully, this can be achieved without causing unnecessary injury or unnecessarily damaging a relationship.

Simple techniques can be used with little practice:

· **Triceps pinch**: Pinch and twist the skin on the inside of the attacker's upper arm.

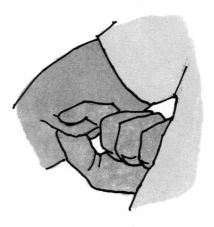

· **Knuckle to sternum**: Apply pressure (not a punch) with the knuckles to the attacker's breast bone, pushing hard and twisting.

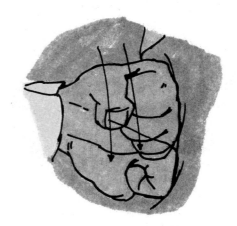

- **Feign injury**: If you emphasise the amount of damage the attack has done to you, your attacker may hold off long enough for you to escape.

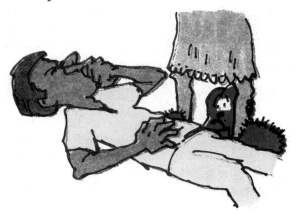

- **Shin scrape**: Scrape the heel of your shoe down the shin of your attacker.

Reporting Incidents of Aggression

Know your organisation's policies for reporting aggressive incidents. You have a duty to accurately report these incidents. Complete any reports of the incident as soon as possible, while events are still fresh in your memory. If you have worries or uncertainties about dealing with aggressive behaviours, seek advice from an appropriate person.

Incidents are generally described on prescribed forms which usually ask for the following information:

- when the incident occurred

- where the incident occurred

- a brief, factual account of the incident, which should include all important happenings at the time of the incident and the names of those immediately involved

- action taken immediately following the incident, including who was informed of the incident

- any injury or damage that has occurred

- any other relevant facts that had a bearing on the incident, e.g., the mental state of the aggressor

Organisational Response to Aggression

Organisations should provide training to manage violent situations so that you are capable of doing your job. Training will help you prevent a person's behaviour escalating to aggression.

A positive organisational response to staff who have been assaulted includes offering support to these victims of assault. Victims often feel guilty and inadequate after an attack. This might also include reporting incidents of violence to the police for criminal investigation or supporting staff to take civil action where the incident does not warrant criminal prosecution.

Check Your Knowledge and Understanding

1. You are on duty alone in a residential home. You hear screaming in the lounge. John is crouched down with his hands over his head, and Mike is stood over him raining punches down onto him. You approach Mike, taking him by the arm, and you tell him to stop. Mike pushes you away and recommences his attack on John. You then grab Mike and pull him away with all your strength. He falls over a coffee table and cuts his head when it hits the floor.

   Which of the following answers is correct?

   a) You are guilty of assaulting Mike.

   b) You should feel guilty because you should have prevented the attack occurring.

   c) You used the minimum force necessary to stop the attack; therefore, you are not guilty of assault.

   d) You should have used more force on your first approach to Mike to stop his attack on John.

2. Fred attends a day centre. He has returned to the centre after lunch in a drunken and abusive state. You and two colleagues, who know Fred well, manage to bundle him outside to "cool off" where he is not a danger to anybody, as agreed in his care plan. You notice that two buttons have been ripped from your shirt.

   You walk up to Fred, put your hand in his face and push him away hard. Fred falls to the floor, scraping his face on the concrete.

   Which of the following answers is correct?

   a) You are guilty of assaulting Fred.

   b) You should have prevented Fred from entering the building.

   c) You are not guilty of assault, but are likely to be disciplined because your push on Fred was unnecessary.

   d) You should ban Fred from the day centre.

3. You call at May's house to help her take a bath. May does not want a bath. But instead of mentioning this to you, she slaps your face. You step backwards and notice that May thinks this incident is funny. You slap her face and leave.

   Which of the following answers is correct?

   a) You are guilty of assaulting May.

   b) You should ensure that you are accompanied next time you visit May.

   c) You are not guilty of assault, but you are likely to be disciplined for slapping May's face in retaliation.

   d) Refuse to visit May in the future.

4. A man with a history of aggressive outbursts who has been kept waiting for his lunch shouts, ''Oi! Hurry up, I want my dinner **now**!'' What would you do?

   a) Ignore him.

   b) Tell him to stop being so abusive and that you will serve him as soon as possible.

   c) Apologise by saying, ''I'm sorry that you have been kept waiting. I bet you thought we had forgotten you. I'll get your meal now.''

   d) Ask him to wait until you can get round to serving his meal.

5. You approach a woman who appears to be upset. You ask if there is anything you can do to help. The woman replies, ''Piss off and leave me alone!''

   What would you do?

   a) Make a note not to approach this woman in the future.

   b) Ignore the woman's warning and gently take hold of her hand in order to start a conversation.

   c) Say, ''I can see you want to be left alone now. I'll come back later.''

   d) Inform your colleagues that this woman can be quite aggressive.

6. You are asked to work in an unfamiliar, long-stay residential home. During the evening you notice one of the residents pacing up and down outside the home, shouting and waving his arms at passers-by.

   What would you do?

   a) Ignore him.

   b) Ask one of the regular home staff how to handle the situation.

   c) Go outside to try and calm the person down.

   d) Tell the person to come inside and stop shouting at people.

See page 122 for answers.

Tips On Evidence Collection

1. Include the work that you completed for the two exercises in this module.

2. If you see or become involved in handling aggressive and/or violent behaviour at work, record the incident. (Be careful to maintain confidentiality by not using the person's real name in the incident record and by keeping the report safely locked away.) Write an analysis of your feelings during the incident, and evaluate your own performance.

3. If you receive any training on control and restraint or break-away techniques, keep the details in your portfolio.

4. If there are any local policies on the management of aggression, keep a copy of the policies in your portfolio.

Module 3 References

Department of Health and Social Security (1933) **The Children and Young Persons Act**. HMSO: London.

Department of Health (1990) **Code of Practice: Mental Health Act 1983**. HMSO: London.

Department of Health and Social Security (1983) **Mental Health Act**. HMSO: London.

Department of Health and Social Security (1988) Advisory Committee Report: **Violence to Staff**. HMSO: London.

Dingwall R (1984) **Who is to blame anyway?** Nursing Times, April 11, 42-43.

Farrell G A & Gray C (1992) **Aggression: A Nurse's Guide to Therapeutic Management**. Scutari Press: London.

Wondrak R (1989) **Dealing with Verbal Abuse**. Nurse Education Today, 9, 276-280.

Module 4

Unit Z4

- a core unit of the Level 3 NVQ/SVQ Award in Care

Unit Z4 is primarily concerned with the assessment of communication skills and the promotion of communication with people when there are communication difficulties.

Overcoming Communication Difficulties

Promote communication in people who have communication difficulties.

Objectives:

- ☐ Identify common communication problems.
- ☐ Outline how to assess a communication problem.
- ☐ Describe the important aspects of planning care for people who have communication problems.
- ☐ Describe how to overcome physical barriers to communication.
- ☐ Outline the care of hearing aids and spectacles.
- ☐ Explain the use of Makaton.

Module 4 Glossary

aphasia	difficulty using or under-standing words	rapport	harmonious accord, relationship that makes communication possible or easy
articulation	ability to speak clearly		
modulation	adjustments and regula-tion of the tone of voice during conversation	stroke	condition where damage to the brain has impaired the function of one side of the body

Part 1   Establishing Communication Abilities *(Z4.a)*

Consider each person's needs and level of understanding.

There are many potential problems of communication which are encountered in care settings:

· people who only speak in a foreign language that nobody in the care setting can understand

· people who are confused and/or disoriented

· people who are unwilling to communicate, for whatever reason

· people who cannot or will not tell the truth

· people who have sensory problems, e.g., deafness

· people who cannot articulate clearly, e.g., speech defects, stroke victims, etc.

· simple misunderstandings and misinter-pretations

· environment not conducive to communica-tion, e.g., too noisy or not private

· strong emotions and feelings that interfere with communication, e.g., anger, distress, prejudice

Problems of communication can interfere with the provision of good quality care. The following examples could be the result of poor communica-tion:

· non-compliance with the requests of care staff

· misunderstandings that lead to lack of trust

· distress caused by not being able to communicate well

· reduction in a person's self-esteem

· difficulty in assessing other problems

Assessing Communication Problems

To accurately assess communication problems, there is a need to develop rapport. The best way to build rapport is by generating empathy with the other person. This involves listening to what the other person has to say and, more importantly, watching what the person does. While a person may say how he or she is feeling, non-verbal communication provides clues to how the person is really feeling.

Assessing communication problems can be difficult because of the time needed to carry out an accurate assessment. Carers often have many people that require their care, limiting the amount of time that can be spent with one person. The time is further limited by other activities (e.g., the need to keep accurate records, answering the telephone, etc.).

An easy, but structured, way of assessing a communication problem is by writing notes under the following three headings: reception, perception, and expression.

Reception, e.g.,:

- vision and hearing
- concentration span
- ability to discriminate
- level of interest, motivation
- effects of previous learning

Perception, e.g.,:

- ability to remember
- comprehension, understanding of what is being said
- ability to interpret non-verbal communication
- vocabulary, understanding of long words, medical jargon, etc.
- language used, including accent

Expression, e.g.,:

- non-verbal communication (gestures, hand signs, eye contact, posture, interpersonal distance)
- articulation and modulation
- tone, pitch, strength, volume, speed of voice
- interpersonal skills
- ability to listen

It is often appropriate to seek further information about a person's communication abilities by approaching other sources, e.g., family, friends, other professionals. This can help to determine the correct method of communication to use.

Assessing Communication Skills

Communication skills are usually assessed in more detail after a communication problem has been identified by the care staff.

Sometimes a person is known to have good communication skills, but simply chooses not to use them. Or the situation may prevent the person from using good communication skills.

Detailed assessments are usually carried out by a Speech Therapist. The only time communication skills assessments are carried out by care staff is when they are part of a larger assessment of a person's general abilities or level of development. Examples include Portage checklist for the assessment of a child's level of development (Bluma et al, 1976), Progress Assessment Chart for the assessment of the abilities of people who have learning disabilities (Gunzburg, 1977).

Exercise

Choose a person with whom you feel you have difficulty communicating (client, colleague, friend, relative). Assess the communication difficulties as objectively as possible. Determine where communication problems are located:

- in your reception, perception, or expression?

- in the other person's reception, perception, or expression?

- in both of you?

Examine the way(s) that you currently try to deal with the communication problem. Then answer the following questions.

- Does the way that you currently attempt to deal with the communication difficulties tackle the problems that you have identified in the reception, perception, or expression of both yourself and the other person?

- If the answer to the first question is "no," is there anything that you could do to tackle the problems of reception, perception, or expression that are not being addressed? If unsure, seek advice.

Formulate a plan to overcome communication difficulties between yourself and the other person. Try out your plan and evaluate your success. Write up your assessment, plan, and evaluation for inclusion in your portfolio.

Part 2   Assisting Individuals In Communication *(Z4.b)*

Provide whatever help is needed to enable a person to communicate.

Before planning commences, the level and type of assistance needed by the person should be established by assessment. Care strategies should be appropriate to the person's level of understanding and preferred mode of communication. The carer should try to use both verbal and non-verbal skills, as appropriate, that are consistent with the person's own expression and use.

Preferably, different methods of overcoming the communication problem should be identified in the care plan. Aids to communication should be made available where possible, e.g., notepad and pencil, computer, flashcards, etc.

Communication used by care staff should be consistent with the plan of care and delivered at an appropriate pace and level of understanding. Create opportunities for the person to communicate, e.g., during leisure activities and while care is being provided. Encourage, stimulate, and interest the person in order to promote communication. When the plan of care includes recording of the person's communication skills, be clear, concise, and objective. Be aware of the times when the person, appropriately, may not want to communicate. Be aware of, and sensitive to, any conflicts between the care plan and the person's choice of communication. For example, the plan of care might be to stimulate the person to speak, but the person might be too embarrassed to demonstrate a speech impediment.

Be aware of ways to assist with communication:

· Ensure that other professionals are used, where appropriate, e.g., speech therapist, interpreter, psychologist.

· Do not forget that concepts are often difficult to translate into other languages and sign language.

· Do not be afraid to modify a message for a person so that it can be understood.

Various methods of communication are available to support individuals who have communication difficulties. The methods are based on each person's needs and level of understanding. Modify communications as needed.

Physical Barriers to Communication

The following guidelines will help you to interact with people who have physical barriers to communication.

Aphasia

Aphasia is the loss of ability to speak or understand words. Medical problems can affect the area of the brain that deals with language, making communication difficult and frustrating. Therefore, to communicate with people who suffer from aphasia, the following strategies are useful:

· Be patient!

· Use communication aids (e.g., pictures, paper and pencil).

· Eliminate unnecessary noises (e.g., TV, radio).

· Ensure that the person can clearly see your face.

· Address the person by name.

· Speak slowly and use simple words.

· Make the message clear, without too many details.

· Allow time for the person to respond.

· Be supportive and positive.

· Talk normally; do not "talk down" to the person nor shout.

· Ask the person to repeat, if necessary, rather than pretend to understand.

Hearing Impaired

When communicating with people who have impaired hearing, non-verbal communication is more important than verbal communication. There are various degrees of hearing impairment, from slight hearing loss in one ear to total deafness. Therefore, to communicate with a person who has hearing problems, use the following strategies:

· Get close to the person and speak loudly enough to be heard without shouting.

· Speak to the side where the hearing is best.

· Maintain eye contact.

· Ask for feedback to check for understanding.

· Eliminate unnecessary noises (e.g., TV, radio).

· If the person uses a hearing aid, make sure that it is being worn and that it is clean.

· Make sure you face the person who reads lips and that your face is clearly visible (not in shadow).

· Use gestures when appropriate.

Visually Impaired

When communicating with people who have impaired vision, verbal communication and touch are important. There are varying degrees of visual impairment, from slight visual loss in one eye to total blindness. Therefore, to communicate with a person who has visual problems, use the following strategies:

- Identify yourself when entering the room.
- Explain what you are going to do.
- Ask for feedback.
- Remind people who need spectacles to wear them, and offer to clean the spectacles if necessary.
- Use "touch" as appropriate.

Sensory Aids

Sensory aids contribute to a person's well-being and independence. Aids help people to rely more on themselves and less on others. Encourage people to use their sensory aids. Be sure that each person knows how to use the device. Keep devices clean and ensure that they are in good condition, if people are not able to do this for themselves.

Hearing Aids

Be cautious when handling hearing aids because they are fragile. Avoid accidentally dropping a hearing aid by using a table or desk for cleaning the device or for changing batteries.

Keep hearing aids dry, as water and damp ruins them.

- Remove hearing aids before showering or swimming.
- If the hearing aid gets wet, dry it with a soft cloth; never use heat.

Keep hearing aids clean.

- Never use water, alcohol, or cleaning solvents.
- Remove the hearing aid before using hair spray.
- Use a soft cloth.
- Never use oil.
- Never use sharp instruments, e.g., paper clips, pen knives.

Extend the life of batteries as they are expensive.

- Turn off the hearing aid when not in use.
- Disconnect the battery contact for storage during the night.
- Remove the battery if the aid is not to be used for more than 24 hours.
- Check to ensure that the battery is working before placing the device in a person's ear.

Store hearing aids in a safe place.

- Always use a case for storing the hearing aid.
- Mark the case with the person's name.
- Never leave a hearing aid where children can play with it.
- Discourage the person from putting the hearing aid in a pocket as it may get sent to the laundry with the clothing.

Hearing Aid Trouble Shooting

Problem	Possible Cause	Action
Doesn't Work	dead battery plugged earmold	replace battery clean earmold
Not Loud Enough	low battery plugged earmold hearing may have changed	replace battery clean earmold have hearing checked
Distorted	low battery	replace battery
Fuzzy	faulty hearing aid	check with supplier
Goes On and Off	bad battery faulty hearing aid	replace battery check with supplier
Causes Discomfort	improperly placed wrong style	check placement check with supplier

Spectacles

Spectacles are often misplaced and easily broken. Protect spectacles from loss or damage, and encourage people to wear them if they need them.

You can help prevent damage or loss:

· Clean spectacles with a soft cloth, rather than a paper tissue which can scratch plastic lenses.

· Engrave the person's name on the inside of the frame.

· Ensure that there is a case for storing the spectacles.

· Provide a neckstrap to keep spectacles within reach.

· Check spectacles regularly for loose or missing screws and nose pieces.

Alternative Methods of Communication

Some people have severe disabilities which force them to use alternative modes of communication. For example:

· Packs of flashcards: each card usually highlights a commonly used word, e.g., toilet. When the person wants to communicate, a card is simply held up.

· Communication boards: the boards usually have a series of pictures in squares to which the person can point in order to communicate.

· Computers are often provided for people with the most severe disabilities. The computer can be operated by various means, e.g., a blowpipe, pointer attached to the forehead, eye movements, keyboard, etc.

Makaton

Makaton is a vocabulary based on British Deaf Sign Language. Only key words have to be learned, reducing the demands on those with limited memory. Many of the signs resemble the object or activity of the words they symbolise. The system makes it possible for people who have difficulty with fine movements to make a satisfactory attempt at communicating with signs.

Makaton vocabulary is comprised of a special selection of the most essential and useful words for basic communication. It is structured in stages of increasing complexity. Initial stages include basic vocabulary to express essential needs. Subsequent stages expand the range of signs so that more complex language can be used. If a person can manage initial stages of the vocabulary, the person has acquired a useful, though limited, vocabulary.

Only the key words are signed, but signs should always be accompanied by normal speech. There are no strict rules regarding the precise performance of the signs, e.g., size and distance from the body. The signs should be accompanied, where appropriate, by a suitable facial expression, especially when conveying emotions. A one-handed version of the sign system is available for deaf people who also have physical handicaps.

If you provide care for a person who uses Makaton, it is worth learning at least the early stages of the vocabulary.

Exercise

Find care plans that relate to communication/interpersonal difficulties. Then answer the following questions:

· Are there any people in your care who have communication difficulties, whose problems have not been identified and/or do not have plans of care to overcome or cope with the problems?

· For people who have plans of care that cover communication difficulties, does the planned care adequately deal with the problems?

Where a person does not have a plan of care to deal with communication difficulties that you have identified, prepare a proposed plan of care.

Where the plan of care is inadequately dealing with a person's communication difficulties, write a proposal on how the care plan could be adapted or re-written to deal with the problem.

Discuss your proposed care plans with your manager and/or your NVQ/SVQ Assessor and ask for feedback. Include all the written work that you have prepared for this exercise in your portfolio.

Check Your Knowledge and Understanding

1. Which of the following are communication problems?

   a) A person speaks a foreign language that you do not understand.

   b) A person is not telling the truth.

   c) A person has misinterpreted what you have said.

   d) A person is distressed and angry.

2. A person in your care is a little confused. She is to be discharged home this afternoon. She needs to know about her medication that has been prescribed for her to take home. She also needs to know about the place that has been organised for her at a day centre.

   What would you do?

   a) Inform the lady about her discharge plan and hope that she understands and remembers the information.

   b) Inform the lady, and then write the details down on a sheet of paper for her to keep as a reminder.

   c) Do not inform the lady. Inform the relative who will soon arrive to take her home.

   d) Inform both the lady and the relative, and provide them with the sheet of paper with all the details.

3. Which of the following categories is not used for assessing a communication problem?

   a) expression

   b) reception

   c) conception

   d) perception

4. In planning care to overcome a communication problem, which of the following is incorrect?

   a) A full assessment of the communication problem should be carried out before the care is planned.

   b) The person should be forced to speak English.

   c) You should try to encourage a distressed person, who is not yet ready to talk, to discuss potential answers to his personal problems.

   d) Preferably, different methods for overcoming the communication problem should be identified in the care plan.

5. When communicating with someone who has impaired hearing, which of the following is incorrect?

   a) Shout loudly enough so you can be heard.

   b) Maintain eye contact.

   c) Make sure the person is wearing a hearing aid.

   d) Face the person who reads lips.

> ## Tips On Evidence Collection
>
> 1. If you attend a workshop on communication difficulties or Makaton, include details of the workshop in your portfolio.
>
> 2. If you are actively involved in planning care for people who have communication difficulties, copy a selection of the care plans for inclusion in your portfolio (ensuring that names on the care plans have been erased to maintain confidentiality).

6. Which of the following should you ALWAYS encourage people to do in the care of their spectacles?

   a) Ensure that spectacles are stored in an appropriate case when not in use.

   b) Clean spectacles regularly with a tissue.

   c) Check spectacles regularly for missing screws and nose pieces.

   d) Provide neck straps so that spectacles are kept within reach.

See page 122 for answers.

Module 4 References

Bluma S et al (1976) **Portage Guide to Early Education: Checklist**. Portage Project, CESA: Wisconsin.

Gunzburg H C (1977) **PAC Manual, Volume 1**. SEFA Publications: Stratford-upon-Avon.

Module 5

Unit Z8

· a core unit of the Level 3 NVQ/SVQ Award in Care

Unit Z8 is primarily concerned with preventing distress and supporting people in times of distress.

Supporting Distressed Individuals

People need your support when they are distressed.

Objectives:

- ☐ Recognise components of stress.
- ☐ Describe strategies for the management of stress.
- ☐ Describe essential features of a crisis.
- ☐ Outline how to provide help during a crisis.
- ☐ Describe care needed by a person who is dying.
- ☐ Identify stages of grief.
- ☐ Describe phases of a therapeutic relationship.
- ☐ Outline essential skills for client-centred counselling.
- ☐ Describe various types of counselling.

Module 5 Glossary

crisis	a point in time when an urgent and stressful situation is overwhelming to a person	therapeutic relationship	enabling relationship in which a carer helps another person to meet his or her own needs
mental defence mechanism	mental distortion of fact to protect oneself from stressful thoughts and feelings	unconditional positive regard	relationship in which warmth, acceptance, and empathy are freely given
stress	unpleasant emotional experience linked to dread, anxiety, annoyance, etc.		

Part 1   # Preventing Distress *(Z8.a)*

Help people to manage their stress.

Stress is an unpleasant emotional experience associated with elements of fear, dread, anxiety, irritation, anger, sadness, and grief. Stress is unavoidable. It is the ability to cope with stress that is important.

Before you can help other people cope with their stress, it is important that you understand the different components of stress. Each of the four components highlighted in the model, is an area in the stress process where intervention can be focused.

Model for Understanding Stress

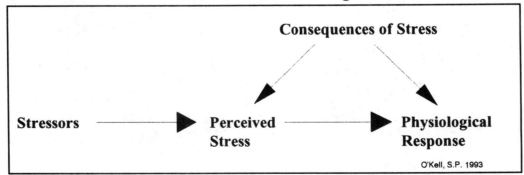

Stressors → Perceived Stress → Physiological Response

Consequences of Stress

O'Kell, S.P. 1993

Stressors

Stressors are physical and/or emotional demands made on a person by his or her environment. Stressors tend to be of two main types.

Major stressors are severe stressors or intense pressures, e.g., death in the family, divorce, redundancy, etc.

Minor stressors are the many small problems that occur during a normal day, often referred to as hassles, e.g., disappointments, traffic jams, etc. Most minor stressors can be easily coped with, but the cumulative effect of repeated exposure can be highly stressful.

Perceived Stress

A person's perception of a stressor is the key to understanding why people respond differently to the same stressor. The two main components of perceived stress are the person and the situation.

Personal factors include:

· values

· attitudes

· personal goals

· personality

Situational factors include:

· duration of stressor

· perceived level of control over the stressor

· available social support

Physiological Response

The physiological response starts with the brain perceiving a stressor that is strong enough to stimulate the sympathetic nervous system to release adrenaline into the bloodstream. If the stressor is strong enough, the level of adrenaline causes the characteristic "fight or flight" response, which is essential for personal survival. Usually stressors stimulate the release of lower levels of adrenaline.

Adrenaline prepares the body for action by making the heart beat faster and sending a greater proportion of blood toward the brain and muscles. Increasing levels of stress can improve a person's performance, but only until the optimum level of arousal has been reached. Beyond this point, performance deteriorates as increasing levels of stress are experienced. When stressors occur over a long period of time, the body becomes worn out by having to deal with the increased levels of adrenaline in the blood.

Consequences of Stress

Consequences of stress fall into five categories: health, psychological, behavioural, occupational, and social.

Effects on health: There is an unusually high risk of developing physical illness (e.g., high blood pressure, heart attacks, stomach ulcers, insomnia, etc.) for people with high-stress occupations and people who experience major stressors.

Psychological effects: Emotions intensify (e.g., anger, helplessness, guilt, feeling unable to cope, vulnerability, etc.), or there is an inability to think clearly (e.g., problem-solving, mental defence mechanisms).

Behavioural consequences: There might be over-reaction (e.g., increased expressions of mistrust, pettiness, anger, etc.); or overindulgence (e.g., increased consumption of tobacco, caffeine, food, alcohol, drugs, etc. used as a crutch to ''get through the day'').

Occupational consequences: There might be general lowering of efficiency and effectiveness at work, with increased errors and reduced productivity.

Social consequences: There might be difficulty maintaining relationships or lack of energy to enjoy life.

Managing Stress

Strategies for managing stress use the main components of stress as the focus. Not all the strategies will be appropriate for all people in all situations. The aim is to find the right blend of coping strategies to help each individual cope with stress.

Coping with Stressors

Although stress is unavoidable, it is sometimes possible to eliminate, reduce, or avoid stressors. For example, the stress of traffic jams and finding parking spaces can be avoided by taking the train. The stress that can sometimes be produced by a care environment can be escaped by opting for home treatment. Unfortunately, some stressors cannot be avoided, e.g., death of a relative.

Coping with Perceived Stress

To cope with perceived stress, self-awareness is important. The aim is understanding and acceptance of self. When this has occurred, the person is ready to deal with the stress.

One useful way of coping with perceived stress is to think about the stressful situation in more positive terms. For example, being made redundant could be viewed as an opportunity to start a new, more worthwhile career.

Coping with Physiological Response

If the body is slowly wearing out due to increased levels of adrenaline in the blood, reduce the level of adrenaline that is released by the sympathetic nervous system. This is done by stimulating the parasympathetic nervous system. There are two main ways of triggering the parasympathetics: physical exercise and relaxation.

- **Physical exercise** triggers the system directly. The exercise should be enjoyable, rather than competitive and overdone.

- **Relaxation** triggers the system indirectly via the use of relaxation techniques, meditation, deep breathing, massage, etc.

Coping with the Consequences of Stress

Following are suggestions for coping with the consequence of stress:

- **Personal health:** Exercise and healthy eating help to burn off adrenaline and prevent the build-up of cholesterol in the arteries.

- **Creative use of leisure time:** Preferably this should include active physical and mental activity to take the mind off problems.

- **Social networks:** Good interpersonal relationships with friends and family can help a person to talk through problems and receive appropriate support.

Exercise

What do you do to cope with the stress in your life? Describe your preferred coping strategies under the following four headings:

· coping with stressors

· coping with perceived stress

· coping with the physiological response

· coping with the consequences of stress

Then ask yourself the following questions:

1. How easily do I cope with stress?

2. Am I happy with the type and amount of coping strategies that I am using?

3. Do I need to make any changes to my lifestyle?

Part 2   Supporting People in Times of Distress *(Z8.b)*

Good communication skills are essential for supporting people who are distressed.

Crisis refers to a turning point or a decisive moment in time when a person is faced with an urgent and stressful situation which feels over-whelming (Parry, 1990).

A crisis includes the following essential features:

· **stress event**, e.g., death of a spouse, any long-term stressor, severe financial problems

· **distress**, i.e., a stressor that is perceived as being very stressful

· **loss, danger, or humiliation**, e.g., loss of a career when made redundant, humiliation when caught shoplifting

· **inability to control** the situation

· **unexpected event**, e.g., the woman who has just discovered her husband is having an affair

· **disruption of routine**, e.g., being made redundant means you do not have to get up to go to work

· **uncertainty** about the future, e.g., your home has been repossessed and you do not know where you are going to be living

· **distress that occurs over time** (typically two to six weeks)

Exercise

Think back to a time when you had a personal crisis. Write down all the details of the crisis that you can remember. Check that all essential features of a crisis are involved in your crisis. If they are not, the likelihood is that your situation was a very stressful event, but not a crisis.

A person's response to crisis can include any of the consequences of stress mentioned earlier. In addition, there are various other feelings that people often experience:

- **not real**: a short-term feeling that the situation is not real and that they will waken from a dream

- **anaesthesia**: a short-term feeling of numbness caused by shock which results from the release of chemicals in the body that protect a person from pain

- **avoidance or pre-occupation** with the problem

- **anger, shame, and guilt**

Some people feel so depressed that they want to harm themselves. These people are usually kept under close observation whenever possible. Make sure you know your organisation's policies on managing people who want to harm themselves.

It is also important that you do not become too involved. Know when to ask for help when dealing with people in crisis.

Providing Help During a Crisis

Coping with crisis can be very difficult, especially when there is inability to think clearly and solve problems. It is important to assess the help that a person needs during a crisis.

The required help can usually be placed into one of four categories: emotional support, information or advice, companionship, or practical help (Parry, 1990).

- **Emotional support**: Be there for the person, to provide physical contact and a safe environment in which to express emotions.

- **Information**: Provide information and advice. (E.g., ''It is only natural that you still feel so ashamed after your experience. You might want to consider a visit to the Citizens Advice Bureau. They will really understand what you are going through.'')

- **Companionship**: The social network is important in re-establishing a grip on reality. Contact with other people ensures that there is somebody with whom the person can talk or spend time and take his or her mind off the problems.

- **Practical help**: Provide help with simple tasks such as washing, ironing, or shopping.

Death and Bereavement

Death and bereavement are important crises which affect almost everyone at some point in life. You may have to care for people who are dying. Do not allow your fear of death to stop you from being sensitive to the needs of the dying person and the person's family.

Caring for Someone Who is Dying

Follow these guidelines when providing care for someone who is dying:

- Make the person as comfortable as possible.

- Continue normal care.

- Encourage the person to suggest how he or she could best be supported. This might include not leaving the person alone, or keeping the room well-lit if darkness is frightening to the person.

- Talk in a normal voice.

- Do not tiptoe.

- Provide comfort and support for the person and the family, as required.

- Respect the need for time and privacy with close family and friends.

- Provide spiritual support if requested.

- Allow the person to die with dignity.

Exercise

This exercise may be painful, especially if you have recently lost a loved one. Do not worry if you cannot attempt this exercise at the moment. If you do attempt the exercise and you find it very upsetting, do not be afraid to seek help to come to terms with your feelings.

If you have lost a loved one in the past, think about how you felt. Consider how the death was handled by the family, friends, and medical staff. Reflect on what comforted you and what upset you.

Make a list of the good and bad things that happened. Then consider how these two lists could translate into providing appropriate care for a dying person and the person's family.

Stages of Grief

People who believe they are about to die react in different ways. Moods may change from day to day as they grieve over life ending. Family members often experience the same feelings.

In her work with dying patients, Kubler-Ross (1969) identified five stages of grief: denial, anger, depression, bargaining, and acceptance. The stages apply to any major loss.

Not everyone goes through all five stages, nor is there a specific order. Some may repeat stages. Being familiar with the five stages of grief will help you to understand what the person and the family are experiencing.

Denial is a state of shock when the person cannot accept what is happening. The person may insist it is a mistake or may ignore the facts completely.

- Do not force the person to face the truth.

- Give people time to adjust.

- Listen when people want to talk.

- Do not force conversation.

Anger is normal. People express anger at God, at the doctor, at life, perhaps even at you. They may yell at you, accuse you of poor care, complain about everything, or refuse to do anything you ask.

- Be patient.

- Continue giving the best care you can.

- Do not take insults personally.

- Do not become defensive.

Depression happens when people have partially accepted death. People become discouraged and sad. They are sorting out their feelings. Sometimes people become very withdrawn and may not want to eat or socialise. Others become more talkative and need more of your time.

- Being there for the person is very important. If he or she wants to talk, listen patiently.

- Be compassionate. If the person does not want to talk, do not force conversation.

- Give the best care possible.

Bargaining is when people try to make deals to postpone death. They will bargain with God or the doctors. Sometimes they may try to bargain with you.

- Listen with a caring attitude.

- Never make promises or say "Things will be alright."

- Let the person know you are there for them.

- Hold the person's hand for comfort.

Acceptance is when the person accepts that death is inevitable. It does not mean that he or she wants to die. The person may be talkative or may be very quiet. Spending time with close relatives or friends may be very comforting for the person.

- Be there to hold a hand and keep the person from feeling alone.

- Continue routine care.

- Provide privacy with loved ones.

- If a member of clergy is requested, let the person-in-charge know immediately.

Therapeutic Relationships

A therapeutic relationship pertains to a long-term relationship between a carer and a person receiving care. Therapeutic relationships can be very stressful because working closely with people who are highly stressed is very demanding. The relationship does not happen automatically and is only achieved after a lot of hard work in developing the relationship.

Three phases of a therapeutic relationship were identified by Ironbar and Hooper (1989): introductory, working, and termination.

Introductory Phase

On meeting, both parties tend to appraise each other, forming their initial impressions of each other. The carer needs to demonstrate:

- **confidence**: via appropriate verbal and non-verbal communication and showing competence in the job

- **warmth**: via showing genuine concern, personal recognition, respect and support for the other person

Working Phase

The quality of the relationship directly affects how effective the carer can be in helping the person work through personal problems, maintain individuality, and learn from the experience. The carer uses counselling skills to develop the relationship.

The most important aspect of this phase is to develop empathy. You need to accurately perceive the feelings of the other person and understand what that person is trying to communicate to you (Tschudin, 1989). This provides the foundation for planning the way ahead.

Termination Phase

Sooner or later, the relationship with the carer will have to end. It is important to use this experience positively as the person regains autonomy and personal control over his or her own life.

Counselling

Listening is an important communication skill used within counselling. You can provide help and support by being an understanding listener. Create a climate in which the person needing help feels accepted and confident enough to be able to talk freely about thoughts and feelings without having to be defensive. As a result of being able to talk freely, a person can gain greater insight into the problem and be able to resolve the problem or cope better with the situation.

The counsellor does not offer ready-made solutions or answers. The counsellor encourages the client to think things through and work out his or her own solutions to problems. This is a difficult process as there are often strong emotions in the client and counsellor to be handled. Therefore, before you take on any formal counselling, it is important that you receive the appropriate training in counselling skills.

Non-directive, client-centred counselling has certain pre-requisites that the counsellor has to offer before successful counselling can take place (Brearley & Birchley, 1986):

- **Empathy**: The counsellor, without making pre-judgements, perceives the world as the client perceives it and conveys this understanding to the client, mainly by reflection.

- **Congruence**: The counsellor recognises his or her own feelings so that personal feelings are not allowed to impinge on the relationship (e.g., when talking about a subject that is causing difficulties in the counsellor's own life).

- **Non-possessive warmth**: The counsellor expresses a warm, unconditional concern for the client, whatever his cultural, racial, religious, or political background.

Types of Counselling

Be alert to the different ways that you can support someone who needs help. Listed below are five types of counselling.

- **Developmental**: helps people confront and deal with specific developmental tasks in their lives. The main emphasis is on development of the person, rather than on specific problems or decisions, e.g., promoting self-awareness.

- **Problem-focused**: helps people overcome or learn to cope better with one or more specific problems, e.g., marital disharmony.

- **Decision-making**: helps people to make specific decisions, e.g., choosing a career.

- **Crisis intervention**: helps people who feel overwhelmed and are having difficulty coping. The people are often highly emotional and the counsellor simply works towards getting them over the worst of the crisis, e.g., redundancy.

- **Support**: helps people who are not going through a crisis, but who need extra support to help them through awkward phases in their lives.

Counselling Skills

Counselling involves the use of a wide range of relationship and communication skills:

- Put the client at ease with a welcome and smiling acknowledgement.

- Reassure the client about the boundaries of confidentiality, e.g., the information will only be discussed with other members of the care team.

- Demonstrate active listening.

Use verbal interventions that encourage the client to talk.

- **Restate:** Repeat the ideas of the client in your own words.

- **Reflect:** Accurately identify and reflect back the client's own feelings.

- **Summarise:** Bring together, simply and clearly, the main details spoken by the client.

- **Paraphrase:** Use your own words to rephrase the essential meaning of what the client is saying.

- **Focus on specific issues** that need to be explored further.

- **Ask open questions** (rather than closed questions requiring one word answers), e.g., ''How?'' or ''What if . . .?''

- **Negotiate for meaning** when a person's words do not seem to carry the intended meaning. (Paraphrasing, in this case, is useless.) Say, ''What I think you mean is....''

Use appropriate non-verbal communication:

- **Maintain an attentive and open body posture**, e.g., uncrossed legs, unfolded arms, lean slightly forward to show interest, use appropriate eye contact.

- **Choose appropriate seating arrangements**, e.g., you are not sitting behind a desk, your chairs are at a slight angle to each other.

- **Reflect the person's facial expressions** and provide affirmative head nodding.

Barriers to Counselling

Avoid the following barriers to counselling:

· **Being judgemental:** jumping to conclusions, communicating to the client that to be accepted, he or she must think as you think.

· **Making reassuring statements:** trying to do magic with words, e.g., saying ''Everything will be fine.''

· **Giving advice:** seen as different from supplying the client with information.

· **Changing topics:** including interrupting, usually used to protect the counsellor from having to broach stressful topics.

· **Showing indifference:** fiddling, mumbling, assuming a condescending attitude, or making rejecting statements.

Exercise

If feasible in your work situation, assess your verbal counselling skills. Audiotape an interaction with a client where you have tried to use these skills. Explain to the client that the only reason for the recording is to assess your communication skills. Ensure that you have the client's permission, and guarantee confidentiality.

Afterwards, when you are on your own, listen to the tape. Make note of the good verbal counselling skills that you used and the mistakes that you made during the session. Repeat the process at a later date to see if you are improving.

Check Your Knowledge and Understanding

1. A friend confides to you that his boss is causing him a lot of stress at work, and recently he has started getting palpitations before going into meetings where his boss is going to be present. What is the most appropriate advice to give to your friend?

   a) "Find another job."

   b) "Try learning relaxation techniques to use before each meeting with the boss."

   c) "Try to avoid going to the meetings."

   d) "Go to the pub for some 'Dutch courage' before the meetings."

2. Which of the following is not one of the stages of grief?

   a) bargaining

   b) denial

   c) anger

   d) acceptance

3. You are counselling a teenager who confides that he feels nervous about asking the girl next door out for a date because of his acne. You reply, ''Your complexion is making you worried about asking this girl for a date.''

    Which counselling skill has just been used?

    a) focusing

    b) restating

    c) summarising

    d) negotiating for meaning

4. Which of the following is not an essential feature of a crisis?

    a) depression

    b) disruption of routine

    c) inability to control the situation

    d) anger

5. Which of the following statements are incorrect?

    a) Stress stimulates the parasympathetic nervous system.

    b) Stress is avoidable.

    c) Performance improves in line with increases in stress.

    d) A traffic jam is a major stressor.

6. Which one of the following is not one of the main categories for providing help to people who are in crisis?

    a) relaxation and exercise

    b) information

    c) companionship

    d) practical help

See pages 123 for answers.

Tips On Evidence Collection

1. Include the work that you completed for the four exercises in this module.

2. If you become involved in handling people who are distressed and in crisis, record the incident. (Ensure that you maintain confidentiality.) Describe how you felt, and evaluate your own performance.

3. If you receive any training in counselling skills, crisis intervention, or any other relevant training pertaining to distress, keep the details in your portfolio.

4. If there are any local policies concerned with this area of work (e.g., how to handle people who are likely to harm themselves), you might want to keep a copy of the policies in your portfolio.

Module 5 References

Brearley G & Birchley P (1986) **Introducing Counselling Skills and Techniques**. Faber & Faber: London.

Ironbar N O & Hooper A (1989) **Self-instruction in Mental Health Nursing**. Balliere Tindall: London.

O'Kell S P (1993) **Managing Organisational Stress, Part 1**. Senior Nurse, 13, 3, 9-13.

Parry G (1990) **Coping with Crises**. Routledge Ltd: London.

Tschudin V (1989) **Beginning with Empathy: A Learner's Handbook**. Churchill Livingstone: New York.

Module 6

Unit Y2

· a core unit of the Level 3 NVQ/SVQ Award in Care

Unit Y2 is primarily concerned with enabling people to access and use a wide variety of available services and facilities through the provision of appropriate information, encouragement, and support.

Making Use Of Available Services and Information

Encourage people to access and use available services.

Objectives:

☐ Know the services that are available locally in the public, private, and voluntary sectors.

☐ Identify how people can access information about local services and facilities.

☐ Describe how people can be helped to access services.

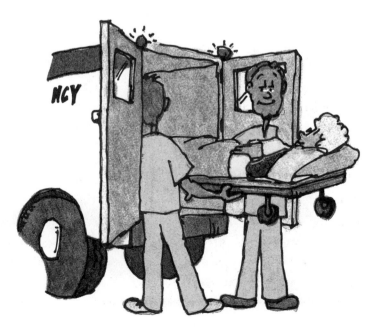

Module 6 Glossary

epidemiology	the scientific study of the distribution of diseases	ophthalmic	pertaining to the eye

Part 1	**Finding Out About Available Services** *(Y2.a)*

Have up-to-date information on available services.

You need to have up-to-date knowledge of the services and facilities that are available to the client group in your area.

All available services are funded from four main sources: taxation, national insurance contributions, donations, and charges or fees. Most public services are mainly funded via taxation and national insurance contributions in varying proportions. Private sector services are mainly funded by charging fees for services provided.

There tends to be a tremendous variation in the provision of available services in different localities. The National Health Service (NHS) and Community Care Act (Department of Health, 1990) has tried to ensure that there is better coordination between the services. But a continuing shortage of resources means that priorities have to be set, and not everyone's needs can be met, especially when there is growth in demand.

Problems facing local services include:

· Population has grown, especially the elderly who consume the most services.

· Rising expectations mean that people are less content with available services.

· New needs and services/treatments are being discovered, e.g., expensive cancer treatments, the need to keep the unemployed occupied.

· Inflation increases the cost of services.

· Family patterns are changing (i.e., more unmarried mothers and single parents, and fewer people who want to look after elderly relatives).

Important information that people need to know about local services includes:

· the types, range, availability, and accessibility of services that are offered by agencies for specific client groups and populations.

· agency office addresses, telephone numbers, and opening times, plus any potential accessibility problems for the disabled, and available public transport routes for getting to the offices.

Public Sector Services

Public services include health services, social services, social security, housing, education, employment, and other services.

Health Services

When it was introduced, the NHS aimed to provide an optimum service, rather than an adequate service. In practice, there are gaps and delays in provision, and standards are often criticised (Byrne and Padfield, 1985).

Health Services provide:

- hospital-based services, e.g., family practitioner services, maternity, surgery, out-patients
- preventive medicine
- dental services
- ophthalmic services

- pharmaceutical services
- ambulance service
- health promotion services
- school health services
- family planning services
- Public Health Department e.g., epidemiology
- home nursing services

- psychiatric services
- learning disability services
- special hospital services for mentally disordered offenders

Social Services

Social Services provide a wide range of services. They are often criticised because of their inability to meet everybody's needs.

- domiciliary (home) services, e.g., **meals-on-wheels, tucking-in**, domestic help, **sitters-in**, laundry service
- aids to living, e.g., home adaptations and **aids**
- day centres and clubs, e.g., for the elderly, disabled, people with learning disabilities
- residential services, e.g., for the elderly, disabled, people with learning disabilities
- transport, e.g., to day centres
- social work services
- fostering and adoption services
- child minder register
- hostels, e.g., for people who have learning disabilities

Social Security

Benefits that can be obtained from social security include:

- family income supplement
- supplementary benefit
- unemployment benefit
- housing benefit
- state pension
- child benefit
- mobility allowance
- severe disablement allowance
- redundancy payments
- invalidity benefit

Difficulty in obtaining benefits is a major problem (Byrne and Padfield, 1985). Problems that people face include:

- ignorance of available benefits
- non-availability of application forms
- complexity of rules and regulations
- obscure language in leaflets
- stigma involved in making claims
- poor customer service skills of the officials

Housing Services

Services include:

- sheltered accommodation
- tenants exchange schemes
- council accommodation

Education Services

Education Services provide:

- local Education Authority schools
- special schools for people with disabilities, e.g., deaf, blind, learning disability, behaviour problems

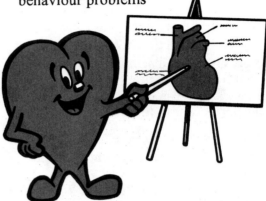

- further and higher education institutions
- home visit teachers
- youth services. e.g., youth clubs and youth organisations (Scouts)
- free school meals and milk
- transport to and from schools

Employment Services

Employment Services provide:

- job centres
- employment training
- sheltered employment
- industrial tribunals
- Enterprise Allowance scheme for unemployed people to start their own businesses
- careers service
- Disabled Resettlement Officer

Other services provided by the public sector are:

- prison service, including borstals and detention centres
- courts of law
- probation service

Voluntary Sector

Voluntary services have some advantages over public services:

- freedom from bureaucracy
- ability to specialise in minority groups, e.g., people who are gay, unmarried mothers, people who have AIDS, the homeless
- flexibility and ability to help those in immediate need

Services include:

- housing associations
- employment bureaux
- sheltered employment schemes
- special schools
- charitable organisations, e.g., NSPCC, Epilepsy Society
- residential homes
- adoption agencies
- shelter for the homeless, e.g., Salvation Army

Private Sector

The private sector is free from bureaucracy but needs to make a profit. Services include:

- residential homes, e.g., for the elderly or mentally ill
- domiciliary services
- community nursing services
- nursing homes
- private medical treatment

Local Facilities

Local facilities are provided by the public, voluntary, and private sectors:

- shops
- post offices
- health clubs/centres
- building societies
- solicitors
- swimming baths
- banks
- cinemas
- churches
- estate agents
- various clubs
- libraries

Obtaining Relevant Information

To assess client needs for information, find a quiet room where you and the client can talk confidentially. Follow these guidelines:

- Use a counselling approach.

- Give the person time and space in which to express his or her needs.

- Discuss available services at a level and pace that is appropriate to the person's abilities.

- Check at intervals for the person's understanding of information being provided.

- Discuss potential sources of information.

Keep the following factors in mind when planning to meet a person's needs for information:

- The person should be encouraged to seek out, and obtain, his or her own information, where practical. If assistance is required, the amount and type of assistance should be negotiated.

- The person should be encouraged to access services that are appropriate to his or her own beliefs and preferences. For example, a person should not be pressurised into putting an elderly parent into a residential home if the person firmly believes that relatives should be cared for by family.

- Any information that is provided for the person should be relevant and up-to-date. The information should be presented at a pace and level and in a format that facilitates understanding. For example, glossy brochures and leaflets are no good to somebody who cannot read well.

When information has been obtained by a person, use a counselling approach (described in Module 5).

- The person should be encouraged to feed back to you any relevant information that he or she has found, including the source.

- The person needs to understand about any restrictions concerning the availability and targeting of services that he or she would like to access. For example, it is difficult to get tucking-in service to put a relative to bed at a precise time.

- You may need to handle the person's reaction to discovering that a service is not available to him or her. For example, searching for alternative services or providing guidelines on how to cope without the service.

- You may find that the person does not want an available service, despite needing it, e.g., the stigma attached to children receiving free school meals. You will need to decide whether to try and persuade the person to accept the necessary service or to accept the person's right to refuse a service.

- You may need to assess the likely effect on overall care of the services that have been chosen. If unsure, seek advice.

Exercise

Be familiar with services that are available for the type of people you serve. Visit the following places:

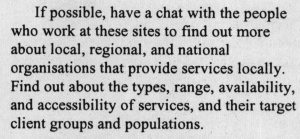

- Citizens Advice Bureau
- Jobs Centre
- Social Services Department
- Social Security Office
- Housing Department
- Local Council Recreational Department
- Health Authority Health Promotions Department

If possible, have a chat with the people who work at these sites to find out more about local, regional, and national organisations that provide services locally. Find out about the types, range, availability, and accessibility of services, and their target client groups and populations.

Maintain an up-to-date folder that contains all the relevant information about the services that are available locally. Keep this folder as part of your portfolio.

Part 2 — Helping Individuals To Use Services *(Y2.b)*

Enable people to use available services.

Factors to bear in mind when supporting a person to access services and facilities:

- Establish with the person the type and level of assistance that is required to access the service, e.g., escort, money, help to decipher timetables, etc.

- Offer an appropriate level of support that enables the person to access the service without leading to unnecessary dependence.

- Accompany the person, if appropriate, in the early days of using the service or facility until confidence is gained. Examples are knowing which bus to catch and the route to walk, providing psychological support to overcome fears, and assisting with communication difficulties.

Problems of Service Access

Access problems should be tackled or challenged. For example, if the only access to council offices is up a flight of stairs, this situation should be challenged to encourage the council to put in a ramp for wheelchair users.

Some people may be at-risk while accessing various services, e.g., risks to members of the public from somebody who is very aggressive, or risks to a person who is likely to get lost. These risks should be assessed by the multidisciplinary team before the plan for accessing services is implemented.

At some stage, you need to evaluate whether the person is using the available information to access appropriate services. This can be done by assessing relevant aspects of the person's life, e.g., cleanliness of the house, relationships that have been formed, financial management, attendance at work, etc. Problems of dependency need to be handled if the person is ever to become as independent as possible in accessing information and services.

Exercise

Choose four people for whom you provide care. Without pressurising these people, ask for their permission to find out about the health, welfare, and other services that they currently access. This will probably involve reading people's case notes and interviewing them about the services that they receive. Reassure them by saying that the object of the exercise is to assess whether they are receiving the appropriate type and amount of services to meet their needs.

For each person, assess:

· level of satisfaction with the type, quality, and quantity of service that is received

· ability to cope with everyday living and ability to experience a satisfactory quality of life

· potential services that each person could or should access if he or she knew about the services and were allowed to access them

Write a report on your findings and discuss your report with your NVQ/SVQ Assessor. Check with your manager before feeding back your findings to the individuals who were assessed and to their key workers. Any criticisms of the services provided need to be handled sensitively. Include the report in your portfolio.

Check Your Knowledge and Understanding

1. Which of the following are significant reasons why resources will not stretch to meet everybody's needs in public sector services?

   a) The public has an increasing expectation of services.

   b) Inflation means that services are becoming more and more expensive.

   c) Family patterns have led to an increase in unmarried mothers and single parent families.

   d) There has been growth in the number of elderly people.

2. During an assessment interview, you discover that one of your clients is claiming unemployment benefit while earning a good wage by working full-time. What would you do?

   a) Advise the person that he or she is breaking the law and highlight the potential consequences of doing so.

   b) Tell the person that you are going to report the issue to the Social Security Department and get the unemployment benefit stopped.

   c) Make an anonymous phone call to the Social Security Department.

   d) Ask the person to refund to you the excess money that has been defrauded so that you can return it to the Social Security Department.

3. Many people do not claim the welfare benefits to which they are entitled. Which of the following is NOT a reason for this:

   a) difficulty in finding welfare benefits offices

   b) people's ignorance of the available benefits

   c) obscure language in welfare benefit leaflets

   d) poor customer service skills of officials who work in welfare benefits offices

4. When helping a person to obtain relevant information about available services and facilities, which of the following are things you should try to AVOID?

   a) providing information when the person has the ability and resources to find out for him/herself

   b) checking the person's understanding of the information provided

   c) providing information that is out-of-date

   d) giving the person time and space to express personal opinions

5. When people are accessing services and facilities, which of the following is NOT appropriate:

   a) Assess the type and level of assistance that is required for accessing.

   b) Do not take any risks.

   c) If necessary, accompany the person on the first two or three visits, until confidence has been gained.

   d) Always inform the person's relatives of the services that are being accessed.

Tips On Evidence Collection

1. Keep all information that you obtain about available services as part of your portfolio.

2. If you become involved in helping people access information and services or facilities, keep a record of your work in your portfolio.

3. If you attend any workshops or study days (e.g., welfare benefits, aids to living, etc.), keep the details in your portfolio.

---

6. Meals-on-wheels, tucking-in, laundry service, sitters-in are all generally referred to as:

   a) Social Security benefits

   b) domiciliary services

   c) community health services

   d) aids to living

See page 123 for answers.

Module 6 References

Byrne T & Padfield C F (1985) **Social Services: Made Simple.** Heinemann: London.

Department of Health (1990) **National Health Service and Community Care Act.** HMSO: London.

Module 7

Unit U4

- a core unit for both the Level 2 and Level 3 NVQ/SVQ Award in Care

Unit U4 is a wide-ranging unit concerned with the promotion of health for all client groups and the maintenance of health, safety, and security. Included here are safe lifting, infection control, health, and environmental emergencies.

Contributing to Health, Safety, and Security

Provide a healthy, safe, and secure environment for the people in your care.

Objectives:

- ☐ Identify areas of concern for health promotion.
- ☐ Explain principles of client security.
- ☐ Outline the management of cash and valuables.
- ☐ Explain how to prevent accidents.
- ☐ Discuss relevant legislation covering health and safety.
- ☐ Discuss how to deal with environmental emergencies.
- ☐ Describe how to lift and move clients safely.
- ☐ Outline principles of infection control.
- ☐ Discuss how to deal with health emergencies.

Module 7 Glossary

acidosis	disturbance of normal metabolism that causes body fluids to become more acid than normal
angina	a severe, but temporary, attack of cardiac pain, usually caused by exercise in people with heart disease
antibody	specific substance produced in the blood, in response to being in contact with a foreign protein, that has a role in the development of immunity
audit	formal inspection and assessment for the purposes of reporting and making recommendations
crepitus	the sound when the two ends of broken bones scrape together
disinfection	destruction of the majority of micro-organisms on inanimate objects by the use of a disinfectant
hyperglycaemia	higher than normal level of glucose in the blood

hypoglycaemia	lower than normal level of glucose in the blood
ketones	substances produced by incomplete metabolism that can cause acidosis
micro-organisms	living organisms that can only be seen with a microscope, e.g., bacteria, viruses, some fungi, etc.
seizure	abnormal functioning of the brain, often including loss of consciousness, caused by abnormal electrical discharges within the brain
sterilisation	process of killing all living micro-organisms, usually by heat treatment
stroke	popular name for a range of circulatory problems of the brain which usually results in hemiplegia (a type of paralysis)
tumour	a swelling caused by a mass of abnormal tissue which fulfills no useful function and can be harmful

---

Part 1	# Promoting Health (U4.a)

Promote health, reduce harm, and control infection.

Health is defined as a state of complete physical, psychological, and social well-being, not merely the absence of disease or infirmity (World Health Organisation, 1948).

Lifestyle has a profound effect on health and well-being. It is never too late for people to change their lifestyles and daily living habits for healthier and happier lives. Preferably, healthy living should start in infancy and continue throughout life.

> **Philosophy of health promotion:**
>
> **PREVENTION IS ALWAYS**
>
> **BETTER THAN CURE.**

Aspects of Health Promotion

Health care workers promote good health for their clients, and the maintenance of a healthy, safe, and secure care environment. For example:

- being concerned with the whole person, encompassing mental, physical, social, emotional, spiritual and societal aspects of health

- accepting that health promotion is a lifelong process, helping people to change and adapt to healthy lifestyles

- being concerned with maximising each person's potential for healthy living

- being concerned with helping people to help themselves by making healthier lifestyle choices

- using a range of formal and informal teaching methods to get the message across

- aiming for a range of health goals which include attitudinal, behavioural, and social change

"Add years to life and life to years" is the aim of the White Paper from Health of the Nation (DHSS, 1986). The idea is to combine public policies, healthy surroundings, and lifestyles, and high-quality health services to improve the health of the nation. There is also a focus on monitoring people's health and researching ways to improve health.

Five key areas for action have been chosen: coronary heart disease and stroke, cancers, mental illness, HIV/AIDS and sexual health, and accidents.

Good health is not just about quality health and social services. It is a partnership between an individual and the health and social services professionals. It should be the responsibility of every citizen to maintain his or her own health.

Your behaviour and appearance are important factors in promoting the health and well-being of others. It is important that you promote your own health.

- Avoid being excessively overweight.

- Practice good personal hygiene.

- Wear appropriate clothing and/or protection.

- Maintain your own physical and mental health; appear healthy.

- Do not smoke or over-indulge in alcohol.

The following information outlines areas where health promotion can be focused.

Smoking

Smoking increases the risk of heart disease, lung disease, circulatory problems, and cancer. Stopping smoking is the most effective action that a person can take to improve health, and it is never too late to feel the benefits.

Help is available. One useful organisation is Action on Smoking and Health (ASH).

Diet

Diet consists of the food a person eats which provides energy and nourishment to live and enjoy life. Everyone needs a well-balanced diet, including plenty of roughage and fluids, enough of the various vitamins and minerals, appropriate proportions of proteins, carbohydrates, and fats, and an appropriate number of calories for size and energy expenditure.

Dietary requirements include:

· Fibre: Include plenty of fruit, vegetables, and other foods rich in fibre. Choose wholemeal rather than white bread. Eat potatoes with skins.

· Fish: Add oily fish like sardines and mackerel to your diet.

· Less saturated fat: Choose white meat in preference to red meat. If you eat red meat, make sure it is lean. Prefer low-fat and fat-free dairy products.

· Less salt and sugar: Avoid eating very salty or very sugary foods.

Refer people to their general practitioners or dietitians if they need detailed advice about their diets or if they have special dietary needs.

Alcohol

Alcohol abuse is a major cause of illness and death. Hazardous drinking is defined as drinking in a way that may cause damage to health and social function (Medical Council on Alcoholism, 1990). Moderate and occasional drinking is usually considered harmless. There are many low-alcohol and alcohol-free products that are available for people to drink, especially if they are drinking and driving.

The primary concern is the amount of alcohol that is consumed. The amount of alcohol is measured in units. It takes approximately one hour to rid the body of each unit of alcohol. One unit equals:

· one single whisky

· one glass sherry or fortified wine

· one glass table wine

· one-fourth pint strong lager

· one-half pint of beer or cider

Low-risk, weekly consumption rate equals:

· 14 units for women

· 21 units for men

Weight

It is not healthy to be either underweight or overweight. The body mass index is a more reliable measure of appropriate weight than weight charts. Body mass index is calculated as weight/height^2 (kg/m^2). For example, if you weigh 100 kilograms and your height is two metres, your body mass index would be 25. A body mass index between 20-25 is acceptable.

Medical conditions resulting from obesity include coronary heart disease, gallstones, diabetes, high blood pressure, etc. Being overweight also contributes to social problems, e.g., exclusion from physical activities, inability to wear fashionable clothes, and society's prejudice against fat people.

Exercise

Exercise is good for people at any age. But, if a person is ill or has been unfit for a long time, it is wise to consult a doctor before undertaking any strenuous physical exercise. Exercise improves strength, stamina, suppleness, and relieves stress.

Everybody has personal preferences for types of exercise. Emphasis should be on a change of lifestyle so that there is uptake of exercise for the rest of one's life.

When undertaking exercise, prevent injuries with an appropriate period of warm up and cool down, including stretching exercises with static stretches (no bouncing). A broad rule of thumb for maintaining a minimum level of fitness is to raise the pulse above 100 beats per minute for at least 20 minutes, a minimum of three times per week.

Sex

Sex is a very normal and healthy part of life. Whatever people's sexual preferences, they should aim for safe and responsible sex. The main danger with unsafe sex is infection. Some infections last a lifetime, and some infections can kill.

You can avoid infection by limiting the number of partners. The more partners, the greater the risk of infections. Never be pressurised into having sex. Think before having sex. If you or your partner have any sores or infections around the genital area or mouth, wait until the infection clears up. Unless you are totally sure that your partner is infection-free, wear a condom. There are varieties for both males and females to wear.

Pass urine and wash your genital area as soon as possible after having sex. This may not be convenient, but you can avoid some infections. If you do get an infection, tell your partner. This may be difficult, but otherwise your partner will keep re-infecting you after you get medical help.

If somebody approaches you for advice on either contraception or infection, refer the person to the Family Planning Clinic or the Genito-urinary Clinic respectively.

Sleep

On average, people spend approximately one-third of their lives asleep. Sleep is a necessary requirement to remain healthy and alert. Not everybody sleeps during the night, e.g., night shift workers. Sleep needs vary. Some people need six or less hours of sleep each night, while others need nine or more hours of sleep.

Many factors influence sleep. A general rule of thumb is that a person can feel whether he or she is getting the required amount of sleep. This should be the yardstick for deciding whether a person gets enough sleep.

Many factors can disrupt sleep patterns, e.g., noise, illness, stress, etc. Advice for helping people sleep usually centres around overcoming or removing sleep-disrupting factors.

Referring and Advising

All care agencies have organisational policies that outline how to provide health promotion and advice. Health promotion plays an important role in the delivery of care:

- If people need advice about their eyes, refer them to an optician.

- If people need advice about their hearing, they should be referred to their general practitioners.

- If people need advice about their teeth, they should be referred to dentists.

- If people need advice about their feet, they should be referred to chiropodists.

- If people have any physical or mental health worries, refer them to their general practitioners (e.g., constipation, skin problems, depression, etc.).

- If people need advice about drug abuse, refer them to general practitioners or a local drug abuse centre, where they can get advice from specialists about their problems.

Always use an acceptable and caring manner when you promote health or offer advice. Respect a person's right to ignore health advice.

Encourage people in your care to ask questions. If you cannot answer a question, admit that you do not know the answer. Refer the person to someone who knows the answer.

When offering health promotion advice, use appropriate discrimination. For example, leaflets for safer sex would probably be inappropriate for people over 70.

All health authorities have health promotion departments that ensure that health promotion materials are available in the care setting. The materials should be relevant and up-to-date, with different language versions available, if necessary.

Exercise

Collect together all the health promotion materials that are available from your organisation for people receiving care. Assess the quality and appropriateness of these health promotion materials for the client group(s) concerned.

If possible, do a wider search for health promotion materials that are more appropriate and/or better quality than those available from your organisation.

Write a report of your findings, and discuss the report with your manager and/or your NVQ/SVQ Assessor. Keep a copy of your report, and maintain a file of health promotion materials for inclusion in your portfolio.

Part 2	**Providing Safety and Security** *(U4.b)*

Take good care of property, possessions, and their owners.

Safety and security of people in your care is very important. The following examples offer legal, clinical, and personal reasons for security.

Legal reasons, e.g.:

· a child provided with a "place of safety"

· a person referred to a regional secure unit for psychiatric assessment

Clinical reasons, e.g.:

· a person who needs regular medication or treatment

· a person with an infection who is isolated

Personal safety reasons, e.g.:

· a person with a learning disability who might wander off and suffer from exposure

· a person who may attempt to take his or her own life

Establishments have different levels and methods of security. For example, a special hospital might lock clients' rooms at night; use cameras, alarms and special lighting; or employ security staff to monitor entrances and exits. In contrast, a psychiatric hospital might only lock up a small area, such as a secure ward, and make regular checks for the presence of clients.

Whatever the level of security of the building, you need to be sure of your legal rights to prevent someone from leaving or entering.

Follow these guidelines:

· Establish rights of entry before allowing callers to enter the premises. If you have an appointments system, stick to it unless there is good reason for not doing so.

· Carefully explain any restrictions on a person's freedom to the person involved, and ensure that all staff know about the restrictions.

· If a client who cannot be prevented from leaving is likely to wander off and be in danger, clearly state in the care plan the level and method of supervision for this person.

Missing Client

If a person goes missing, follow these steps:

· Search the building thoroughly.

· Search the grounds and local areas.

· Ask around the staff and other clients to see if anybody knows where the person might have gone.

If not found, the person-in-charge will have to set in motion the missing person's procedure. This includes making a note of when the person was last seen, when it was noticed that the person was missing, what the person was wearing when last seen, and if there are any restrictions on freedom.

Police need to be contacted, especially if the person is legally not allowed to leave the building or if the person is likely to be in any danger. The police will want the same details as above, plus they will want a description of the person. They will also want to know about any places or people that the missing person is likely to visit and whether the person is dangerous.

81

Ensure that all details concerning the incident are clearly written up in the person's care plan and on any forms that have to be completed.

Safety of Money and Valuables

Encourage people to keep their personal belongings in secure and appropriate places. Discourage vulnerable people from keeping too much money or too many valuables on them. Ensure that you know and follow any policies or procedures for handling money or valuables.

Lock expensive equipment away when not in use. Keep equipment inventory up-to-date so that it is easy to check if something is missing. Mark all expensive equipment by engraving and/or writing a security code in ultra-violet sensitive ink. Secure buildings during the day and night as appropriate.

If valuables go missing or are stolen, the police will almost certainly be called in, and everybody will be under suspicion. Anyone found guilty of stealing will probably be dismissed.

If you have any concerns regarding health, safety, and security, seek advice from an appropriate person, e.g., Health and Safety Officer, Security Officer, Fire Officer, the police.

Exercise

Obtain a copy of your organisation's policies and procedures relating to the safety and security of cash and valuables. Assess the policies and procedures in terms of appropriateness to your area of work and ease of carrying out the procedures. Check whether the procedures work and whether the policies/procedures are followed.

Write a report about your findings for discussion with your manager or your NVQ/SVQ Assessor and for inclusion in your portfolio. If you have any recommendations for change or if you have any queries about the system, in conjunction with your manager, contact the Internal Audit Department for advice.

Part 3   Ensuring a Safe and Secure Environment (U4.c)

Simple precautions prevent serious injuries.

Health and Safety at Work Act (1974) identifies responsibilities for the employer, the employee, and management.

Employee Duties:

· Care for the health and safety of self and others.

· Comply with the requirements imposed on the employer.

· Adhere to instructions in the operation of plant and equipment.

· Use materials only according to recommended procedures.

· Use protective clothing and equipment as directed.

· Never interfere with or misuse anything provided for health, safety, and welfare.

Employer Duties:

· Ensure health, safety, and welfare at work for all employees.

· Provide and maintain equipment and systems that are safe and without health risks in use, handling, storage, and transport of articles and substances.

· Provide information, instruction, training, and supervision for health and safety at work.

Management Responsibilities:

· Maintain a safe environment for all staff.

· Ensure that staff adhere to orders, policies, and procedures.

· Provide training for safe practices and work methods.

· Explain hazards and safe practices to new employees before they commence work.

· Report/record all accidents.

Guidelines in Care Environments:

· Maintain an environment of health, safety, and security based on allowing people who are receiving care to have individual choices in furnishings, activities, etc., that are consistent with organisational policies.

· Take appropriate action immediately whenever a person's health, safety, or security are threatened.

· Dress, behave, and practice personal hygiene in keeping with good health and safety practices, including the use of appropriate protection where necessary.

· Record all accidents and incidents carefully and comprehensively in accordance with local and national policies, and keep your manager informed of events.

· If you have any concerns about health, safety, or security, seek advice from an appropriate person, e.g., your local Health and Safety Representative.

Exercise

Find out who your Health and Safety Representative is, and ask what the role involves. Ask how you should go about auditing a care environment for health and safety. If possible, obtain a copy of the relevant audit form.

Write up the notes of your meeting with the Health and Safety Representative and include them in your portfolio.

Control of Substances Hazardous to Health (COSHH) regulations require employers to assess the risks created at work where hazardous substances are used. Facts that must be identified:

- potential risks from using the substance in the place of work

- how risks are to be managed

- what precautions should be taken

The employer must provide training for all aspects of working with dangerous substances.

Preventing Accidents

The best way to avoid an accident is to be alert to potential hazards. Be alert to any situations that might cause falls, burns and scalds, accidental poisoning, choking, electrocution, etc.

Falls

Falls are a significant cause of injury. The risk of falling is high for older people, usually due to general weakness, paralysis, confusion, dizziness, impaired vision, or other physical problems.

Before making any changes to a person's immediate environment, ask the person for permission. This shows courtesy, as well as being a safety factor.

Be alert to safety hazards, and take extra precautions to protect elderly and frail people from injury. Simple precautions can prevent serious injuries:

- Remove obstacles to walking, such as personal belongings, wires, or equipment.

- Wipe up spills immediately, taking into consideration the substance that has been spilled and the appropriate safe method for disposal.

- Keep side rails up when the bed is occupied by someone who is at-risk of falling out of bed.

- Assist people in and out of the bath as appropriate.

- Use good lighting.

- Lock wheels when moving people to and from wheelchairs.

- Keep items that are used frequently close at hand so that the person does not fall reaching for them.

- Answer the call light promptly so that the person does not try to get up unaided.

- Encourage people who are unsteady to use hand rails and other prescribed mobility aids when walking.

- Assist with walking, if needed.

- Be alert to furniture or objects that pose a hazard.

- Do not allow people's feet to drag on the floor when you are moving them in a wheelchair.

- Do not leave helpless people unattended.

Burns and Scalds

Burns and scalds are preventable:

- Prevent cigarette burns by enforcing smoking policies.

- Make sure bath water is not too hot. Test the water temperature yourself, and let the person who is having the bath test the water.

- Assist people, where appropriate, with hot foods and liquids.

Accidental Poisoning

Accidental poisoning can be the result of carelessness, confusion, or not being able to read labels because of poor vision. Keep all cleansing agents and disinfectants locked in appropriate storage cupboards. Never place them in household food containers; they may be mistaken for food.

Choking

Use these simple precautions to prevent choking:

- Ensure the person is positioned properly for eating and swallowing.

- Supervise people carefully at mealtimes if they are at-risk of choking.

- Encourage people to take smaller bites and to eat more slowly.

Electrocution

Use precautions to prevent electrocution:

- Ensure that all electrical equipment that is brought into the care facility is checked by an electrician.

- Inspect all electrical equipment externally for obvious damage (e.g., frayed wires).

- Operate all equipment according to instructions. If in doubt, ask.

- Always ensure, where possible, that electrical equipment is properly earthed.

- Ensure that people and environments are dry before plugging in equipment.

- Do not overload electrical circuits by using adapters inappropriately.

- Avoid using extension leads whenever possible.

Exercise

Complete a health and safety audit of the care environment(s) in which you work. Write up a report of your findings and discuss the report with your manager and/or your NVQ/SVQ Assessor. If potential dangers are discovered during the audit, it may be appropriate, with the support of your manager, to contact the Health and Safety Representative about your findings.

Promoting Fire Safety

Fire can cause panic to fit and healthy people. For anyone confined to a wheelchair or bed, or who has reduced mobility, a fire can be terrifying. These people will be depending on you for their safety.

Awareness of fire hazards is the first step toward prevention. Three elements are needed for a fire to start. By removing any of these elements, a fire can be prevented or put out:

heat: flame, or spark, or other heat source

oxygen: found in the air people breathe

fuel: any combustible material (items that can catch fire and burn easily)

Alert the person-in-charge if you smell smoke. If a door feels hot, **do not open the door!**

Fire Hazards

Smoking: Never leave smokers unsupervised. Some people cannot handle smoking materials safely by themselves (due to medication, confusion, etc.).

Smoking materials (e.g., cigarettes, pipes, tobacco, matches) should be safely stored when not being used. Strictly enforce the smoking policy and follow these rules:

· Allow smoking in authorised areas only.

· Be careful when you empty ashtrays not to set the rubbish bin on fire.

· Never allow paper cups or rubbish bins to be used as ashtrays. Ensure that ashtrays are non-combustible.

· **Never permit smoking near oxygen that is in use**.

Storage: Never store oily rags, paint cans, chemicals, or other combustibles in closed areas.

Electrical Equipment: Inspect all electrical equipment that you use and report any defects. Do not use faulty or potentially dangerous equipment:

· frayed electrical cables

· overloaded circuits

· overheated equipment

· improperly earthed equipment

Aerosol cans: Never burn aerosol cans, and do not use an aerosol spray near open flames or cigarettes. Containers are likely to explode when they are exposed to heat. Never dispose of aerosol cans in rubbish bags that are to be incinerated.

In Case of Fire

Ensure that you know your organisation's emergency fire procedures:

- Understand fire evacuation procedures and designated assembly points where people can be counted to see if anyone is missing.

- Know the location of all exits and fire doors.

- Know where the fire alarms and extinguishers are located.

- Know emergency telephone numbers.

> **In case of fire, remember:**
> **ARCE**
>
> **A**larm
>
> **R**escue/evacuate
>
> **C**ontain
>
> **E**xtinguish

1. Sound the **alarm.**

2. **Evacuate** the premises and rescue any people in immediate danger if it is safe to do so.

3. **Contain** the fire by closing doors and windows.

4. **Extinguish** the fire, if possible, using the correct extinguisher.

Fire Extinguishers

Different types of extinguishers are used for different types of fires. Be sure you have the correct extinguisher for the fire, or you may make the fire worse and put yourself in danger.

Water (red)	for most fires, except those involving flammable liquids or live electrical equipment
Foam (cream/yellow)	for burning liquids or electrical fires
Powder (blue)	for burning liquids or electrical fires
CO_2 Gas (black)	for burning liquids or electrical fires
Halon (green)	for electrical fires
AFFF (cream/yellow)	for general fires, burning liquids or electrical fires; use as directed for water or foam, depending on the type of fire

Gas Escapes

Whenever you smell gas or you suspect that there is a gas leak, follow these guidelines:

- Open all windows and doors to let in as much fresh air as possible.

- **Do not** do anything that might cause the gas to explode, e.g., light a cigarette, put a light switch on, turn the central heating on or off, etc.

- Ensure the Gas Board are called on the emergency telephone number to ensure that they arrive as quickly as possible to deal with the gas leak.

Part 4   Maintaining Personal Health and Safety (U4.d)

Never take risks with your health at work.

You may be called upon to lift heavy objects, e.g., linen bags. You may have to move people who are receiving care because they cannot or should not move themselves.

Moving people is a major cause of accidents in the care professions. If you have not completed a course on lifting techniques, you should not attempt to move people. Protect yourself and others from injury by using only approved lifting techniques.

Safe Lifting and Moving Techniques

Lifting properly involves how you stand, move, and position your body. Positioning your body-- back, hips and feet-- in a straight line will make lifting easier, prevent injury, and reduce the rate at which you tire.

Use only lifting and moving techniques that you have been taught how to use. Ask for further training if you have any questions or concerns about lifting or moving the people in your care.

If you think you cannot complete a lift or move with the available equipment and personnel, get help before you start. Never risk injury to your back, except in rare circumstances (e.g., preventing a person from falling out of bed).

Respect people's wishes, whenever possible, for lifting or changing their position. Maximise respect and dignity, and minimise any pain, discomfort, or friction during the lift. If you need to change the environment for the lift, ask the person's permission first. Then return the environment to its original state before leaving the room.

Follow these guidelines for lifting and moving:

1. Check to be sure that you have the right person.

2. Encourage the person to help with the move and to be as mobile as possible (within the confines of the chosen lift and the care plan).

3. Tell the person what you are going to do.

4. Wash your hands before and after lifting someone.

5. Provide privacy as appropriate.

6. Prepare the environment for safe moving or lifting.

7. Wear clothing and footwear that allow you to lift safely (e.g., rubber-soled, flat shoes, and loose-fitting clothes).

8. Use appropriate equipment for lifting or moving whenever it is available (e.g., lifting straps).

9. If two or more carers are lifting, one should take the lead to coordinate the lift.

10. After the move or lift, position the person safely and comfortably.

11. Place the call signal, drinks, and any other necessary items within reach.

Shoulder (Australian) Lift

The shoulder lift is the best manual method for moving a person up in bed, or to transfer a person from bed to chair or chair to bed. Two or more carers are required. This lift should not be used for people who cannot sit or for those with shoulder, chest, or upper back problems.

1. Adjust the bed to a height between your hip and knee, and apply the brakes.

2. You and your fellow carer should stand on opposite sides, close to the bed.

3. Help the person to a sitting position.

4. One carer supports the person while the other adjusts pillows, tubing, etc.

5. Stand a little behind the person who is to be lifted, your shoulders level with the person's back, your feet apart and pointing in the direction of the move. Keep your hips and knees flexed, and your back straight and erect.

6. Press your nearest shoulder into the person's chest under the axilla (armpit), with the person's arms resting on the backs of the two carers carrying out the lift.

Moving A Person In Bed

Check the care plan for any restrictions before moving a person who has to remain in bed. People who are unable to move themselves need to be turned often in order to prevent physical problems, e.g., pressure sores. Roll or slide the person on a sheet, rather than lift. Prevent friction on the person's skin because it can damage the skin and be painful.

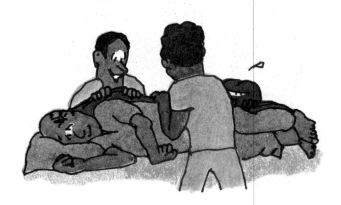

7. Put your nearest arm under the person's thighs, close to the buttocks, using a finger or wrist grip with the carer on the opposite side of the bed.

8. Place your other hand on the bed behind the person, elbow flexed.

9. When the lead carer signals to lift, straighten your rear leg and the elbow of the supporting arm, and shift your weight to the leading leg as you lift.

10. Move the person a short distance at a time, lifting the person clear of the bed to prevent friction injuries. Then bend your leading leg and supporting elbow to lower the person.

If necessary, the lift can be modified. If it is difficult for the person to lift his or her arms, you can place the person's arms between your chest and arm (rather than on your back).

A variety of turning beds is available. However, if there is no turning bed, the procedure requires two carers, one on either side of the bed. The person should be rolled and slid on a drawsheet (not lifted) by the first carer, while the other carer ensures that the person does not roll out of bed and helps with positioning. Another golden rule is to always slide or roll the person toward you, never away from you.

To move a person in bed, begin with the person lying in the middle of the bed on his or her back. Then move the person to one side of the bed in three easy stages:

1. Move the person's head and shoulders toward the chosen side of the bed.

2. Then move the legs in the same direction.

3. Move the trunk to the side of the bed.

The easiest way to move the trunk of the body is by sliding the person on a drawsheet. You may need a second person on your side of the bed if the person is heavy. If a second carer is not available to help you turn the person, always raise the rails on the opposite side of the bed. This is an important safety precaution to ensure that the person does not roll out of bed.

Complete the repositioning of the person who is lying on his or her back to one side of the bed by rolling the person onto his or her side toward the centre of the bed:

1. The person's inside arm is positioned to ensure that he or she is not rolled onto it.

2. The outside leg is crossed over the inside leg.

3. The person is rolled onto his or her side.

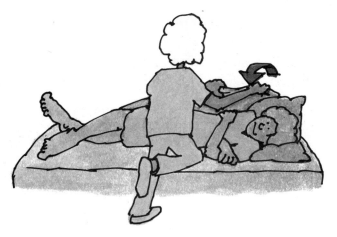

Transfers

Some people need assistance with transfers (moving from one place to another). Check the care plan to ensure that you are not transferring a person to a position which is detrimental to health or comfort (e.g., transferring a person to a chair when they are supposed to remain in bed). Also, check the care plan for the correct transfer technique. When transferring people, encourage them to help as much as they are able. Common transfers include:

· bed to wheelchair

· bed to trolley

· wheelchair to toilet

· wheelchair to armchair

· wheelchair to bath or shower

· bed to armchair

· bed to commode (portable bedside toilet)

Three main types of transfer are: active, assistive, and passive.

· **Active transfer** is used when a person needs minimum help to move from one place to another, e.g., someone who is fully mobile, but occasionally overbalances and falls.

· **Assistive transfer** is used for people who have reduced mobility, e.g., when a person has difficulty standing because of arthritis. The amount of assistance provided will depend on the degree of disability.

· **Passive transfer** is used for people who are unable to help with the transfer; usually because they have paraplegia (paralysis of the legs).

Active Transfer
(moves with minimal help)

Assistive Transfer
(able to help)

Passive Transfer
(unable to help; you need at least
one assistant for the transfer)

Pivot Transfer

The pivot transfer can be used as an active, assistive, or passive transfer. The following description is an assistive pivot transfer to move a person from bed to chair.

1. Identify the person, and explain what you are going to do.

2. Provide privacy.

3. Lock all wheels (bed, wheelchair).

4. Keep transfer sites close together, equalising heights as much as possible.

5. Lower the side rail on the bed.

6. Help the person to a sitting position, with feet over the edge of the bed. Stay with the person to allow time to regain balance.

7. Assist with robe and slippers.

8. Help the person to shuffle his bottom to the edge of the bed. (Be careful that the person does not shuffle too far and slide off the bed.)

9. Stand in front of the person with your feet outside his or hers. Bend your legs (keeping your back straight) and put your arms under the person's arms, around the lower portion of the back, so that you are gently hugging the person. Ask the person to put his or her arms over your shoulders (never around your neck). Alternatively, use a transfer belt.

10. Ask the person to stand, straightening your legs to provide the minimum amount of lift that enables the person to stand.

11. Offer reassurance, especially if the person seems concerned about falling.

12. Slowly turn with the person (without twisting). Be careful not to tread on the person's toes.

13. If required, help position the person properly in the chair.

To transfer the person back into bed, reverse the procedure. Be sure to raise the side rail on the bed, if required. Place all belongings that are likely to be needed within reach before you leave.

Active pivot transfer uses the same procedure, except that you do not hug the person to help him or her stand. Instead, you will hold the person's hands or hold the person's shoulders to steady the person during the transfer.

Passive pivot transfer is usually only used when space restrictions prevent the use of other transfer methods such as slide boards or shoulder lifts. A second carer is always used to help ensure a smooth transfer.

Exercise

1. Contact the staff in your clinical area to ask if they have had any lifting training.

2. Assess the availability of appropriate lifting aids.

3. While working with other care staff, take note of whether they use approved lifting methods.

Write a report on your findings. Discuss your report with your manager and/or your NVQ/SVQ Assessor. Include your report in your portfolio.

The **transfer belt** is used when transferring people who have various degrees of mobility problems. Fasten the belt around the person's waist to provide a grip for you during the transfer. The belt is called a gait belt when it is used to assist in walking.

The **monkey pole** is a swinging bar hanging over the bed from a metal frame. The person grasps the bar with both hands to enable the person to lift his or her bottom clear of the bed to relieve pressure, to move up in bed, to turn in bed, or to strengthen the arm muscles.

The **hydraulic lift** is used for a person who is too heavy to lift. Always have help when operating the hydraulic lift. Make sure you understand how the lift works so that you do not injure the person.

The **slide board** is a small board placed between a bed and a chair at similar heights. The person sits on the board and is helped to slide along the board into the desired position.

A **sheet** is used to transfer people when there is no danger of back injury. Some sheets allow you to insert poles down the edges of the sheet so that a person can be moved by stretcher. Using a sheet to transfer somebody needs at least two carers.

Infection Control

Infection control is critical! By understanding how infection spreads, you can protect yourself and others.

Steps for controlling infection:

· Protect everyone from infection by others.

· Prevent reinfection while recuperating.

· Try to provide surroundings that are free of disease-causing germs.

To protect others from infection, it may not be appropriate for you to work if you have an infection (e.g., a common cold). If there are no clear guidelines, ask your manager. Notify your manager immediately if you are ill with a notifiable disease (e.g., measles).

Infection is spread by micro-organisms (e.g., bacteria, viruses that can only be seen with a microscope). Micro-organisms are everywhere -- in the air, on the skin, in food and beverages, and on everything you touch. Some organisms cause infectious diseases that require the doctor to notify the Public Health Department. so that the prevalence of notifiable diseases (e.g., measles, tuberculosis, etc) can be monitored.

There are two types of organisms:

· non-pathogenic (harmless)

· pathogenic (harmful)

Pathogens are spread in three ways:

· Through the air, via people coughing and sneezing, e.g., common cold, chickenpox, diphtheria, etc.

· By direct contact with another person or by touching contaminated objects, animals, and insects or via ingesting contaminated food or water (e.g., salmonella food poisoning, sexually transmitted infections such as gonorrhoea or glandular fever by kissing)

· Through blood and blood products via injection or via innoculation through broken skin (e.g., AIDS, Hepatitis B Virus, rabies, malaria)

There are many micro-organisms that cause disease:

· bacteria (e.g., mycobacterium tuberculosis causes TB)

· viruses (e.g., human immuno-deficiency virus causes AIDS)

· fungi (e.g., candida albicans causes thrush)

Infection usually enters the body through broken or damaged skin or through the mucous membranes of the eyes, nose, and air passages.

Always report signs of infection:

· fever	· chills
· restlessness	· lack of appetite
· swelling	· redness
· pain	· discharge
· change in behaviour	

Keeping Surroundings Clean

Help control infection with clean surroundings. Keeping the surroundings clean includes cold sterilisation, disinfection, proper linen handling, and isolation.

Sterilisation kills micro-organisms. Unless all micro-organisms are dead, an object is not sterile. A sterile object becomes contaminated when exposed to air or other objects. Diagnostic equipment and metal bedpans are most commonly sterilised by autoclaving (an intense heat process). Cold sterilisation occurs by soaking the object in an approved disinfectant for a set length of time.

Disinfection requires chemicals (disinfectant) that kill most of the micro-organisms. Those that are not killed are slowed in their growth. Reusable plastic bedpans, urinals, and some types of equipment are sanitised (washed in disinfectant), dried, and stored after use.

Linen Handling

Use precautions when handling linen to prevent infection from spreading:

· Hold linen away from you to prevent transferring micro-organisms.

· Avoid shaking or fluffing linen, and keep linen off the floor.

· Wear gloves to handle linen that is soiled with blood or body fluids.

· Place soiled linen in covered hampers or bags to prevent the spread of infection and to control odours.

· Always wash your hands after handling soiled linen.

Isolation

Isolation (setting apart) procedures are used when extra precautions are necessary to control the spread of infection. People with contagious diseases are sometimes isolated to protect others from becoming infected. Isolation may also be ordered for people who cannot fight infection because of old age, illness, or treatment.

Doctors prescribe isolation precautions which vary according to the specific problem that requires the isolation. It is very important to follow isolation procedures.

Signs are posted on the door requiring visitors to report to the person in charge before entering. Surgical gowns, gloves, and masks may be required, depending on the type of infection.

All basic supplies and equipment for the care of an isolated person should be stored in the person's room. Gather any additional equipment before you put on a gown or enter the room.

It is not uncommon for an isolated person to become depressed. You can help prevent depression in a variety of ways:

· Answer the call light promptly.

· Care for the isolated person first.

· Tell the person when you will be back. Try to be prompt, and let the person know if you are going to be delayed.

· Be cautious of what you say outside the room as the person may hear you.

· Help the person, the person's family, and any other visitors to be comfortable and confident with isolation procedures.

· Provide puzzles, books, and other amusements to keep the person occupied.

Washing Your Hands

Hand washing is the most important preventive measure for infection control.

Wash your hands:

· **before and after work**

· **before and after meals**

· **before and after providing care**

· **after using the toilet**

· **after coughing, sneezing, or blowing your nose**

· **after handling bedpans, specimens of body fluids, or human tissue**

· **after handling soiled linen**

Using Protective Barriers

Protective equipment is a barrier between you and sources of infection. Appropriate protective equipment such as masks, gloves, and gowns should be worn whenever you could be exposed to infections.

Gloves

Wear medical gloves whenever you have contact with any of the following:

- people who are bleeding or have open wounds

- blood or other body fluids

- soiled linen

Putting on gloves:

- Check for cracks, punctures, tears, or discolouration.

- Discard if damaged.

- Check that you have access to gloves that are a good fit.

- If a gown is worn, ensure that the gloves are pulled over the gown cuffs.

Removing gloves:

- Hold the glove at the cuff and pull inside out.

- Hold the removed glove in the hand that is still gloved. Then hold the second glove at the cuff and pull that one inside out, enclosing the first glove in the second glove.

- Dispose of the gloves, using the designated bin for infected waste.

- Wash your hands.

Universal Precautions

Universal precautions were developed to prevent the spread of deadly blood-borne viruses and bacteria (Department of Health, 1990). The precautions establish safe practices for care workers to control the spread of Human Immuno-deficiency Virus (HIV) and Hepatitis B Virus (HBV). Because you usually do not know who is infected, you need to take precautions with everyone.

> **Treat everyone with care, but use precautions for each person receiving care, for all used needles, for all body fluids, and body waste. Assume all are potentially infectious. Gloves must be worn at all times when handling these materials to avoid infection.**

Infected people often have no symptoms and may not know they are infected. Therefore, consider yourself at-risk of infection from everyone.

Faeces, urine, sweat, vomit or nose and mouth secretions are sources of cross-infection (infection passed from one person to another).

Gloves

Always inspect gloves before use. Do not use gloves that are torn or cracked, have holes, or are faded. Always wear gloves when you:

- handle blood or body fluids

- tend people with pressure sores, broken skin, rashes, or bleeding

- handle linen soiled with blood, body fluids, or body waste

- clean up spills containing blood or body fluids, using designated cleaning materials

Wash your hands after disposing of the gloves.

97

Needles

Everyone who handles needles must use extra caution:

- Be aware that gloves will not protect you from needlestick injury (pricking yourself with a used needle).

- Dispose of needles in available disposal containers for sharps.

Other Precautions

- If you are pregnant and working in a high-risk area, seek advice from your manager.

- Report all broken skin, any contact with potentially infected materials, and all puncture wounds, according to your organisation's policies.

Hepatitis B

Hepatitis B is a viral infection of the liver. Hepatitis B Virus (HBV) produces fatigue, mild fever, muscle and joint pain, nausea, vomiting, and loss of appetite.

There is no known cure for HBV. Most carriers have no symptoms. A blood test is the only way to find out whether a person is infected. The virus usually spreads through contact with infected blood, blood products, and body fluids.

However, the virus can be found in urine, faeces, semen, tears, saliva, vaginal fluid, and breast milk.

The virus is transmitted primarily through:

- intimate sexual contact

- puncture wounds from contaminated needles or sharp objects

- mucous membranes (eyes, nose, or mouth)

- damaged skin (cuts, rashes, dry skin)

Known cases of HBV do not normally require isolation. HBV sufferers are entitled to courtesy, as well as quality care. At times when extra precautions are needed, explain to the person that extra precautions are needed for the protection of other people. If a person with HBV dies, continue the same precautions you took when he or she was alive.

If you work in areas where you could possibly encounter HBV and have not been vaccinated, contact your manager to ask about getting vaccinated. Vaccination is the only sure way to protect against HBV.

Acquired Immune Deficiency Syndrome

Acquired Immune Deficiency Syndrom (AIDS) is caused by the human immuno-deficiency virus (HIV). AIDS cripples the immune system (the body's natural defense against disease), and an AIDS sufferer usually dies from secondary infections.

AIDS kills! Prevention is the only cure. The best form of defense against AIDS is to be well-informed. Find out all you can about AIDS. Use universal precautions to protect yourself and others from infection.

People at high-risk are those who have:

· unprotected sex

· many sexual partners

· other sexually-transmitted diseases

· injected drugs and shared needles

· had blood transfusions since 1977 with blood products that have not been heat treated.

Since 1985, all donated blood in the United Kingdom has been tested for antibodies (part of the body's defense mechanism) to HIV. Unfortunately, some haemophiliacs who were treated with clotting factor before 1985 have become HIV positive.

When people are infected with HIV, they are carriers for life. Some carriers never show symptoms, but can still transmit (pass on) the virus to others. For this reason, you must treat everyone with caution.

Some infected people develop mild symptoms of the disease a few days after infection:

· flu-like sickness

· swollen glands

· rash

· fever

The symptoms go away, but HIV remains in the body. There is no known cure and no vaccine for HIV. The symptoms of AIDS may develop five to fourteen years later.

The disease is transmitted when infected fluid enters the bloodstream via blood, body fluids that contain blood, semen, and vaginal secretions.

HIV can enter the body through:

· puncture wounds from infected needles or broken glass

· cuts or open sores

· mucous membranes (nose, mouth, eyes)

· intimate sexual contact

· transfusions with infected blood

· infected hypodermic needles

· infected mothers to their unborn babies

Exercise

Obtain copies of your organisation's cross-infection/infection-control policies. Formulate a questionnaire from the documents in order that you can test your colleagues' knowledge of the policies.

Observe your colleagues at work, and compare their methods of working to those outlined in the policies.

Write a report of your findings for discussion with your manager and/or your NVQ/SVQ Assessor. Any concerns regarding infection control should be reported by your manager to the Infection Control Officer.

Part 5 — Responding to Health Emergencies *(U4.e)*

Your prompt action can save lives.

Emergencies happen. Someone's life may depend on you. You must act fast if you are to save someone's life. Be aware that you can worsen the injuries of a casualty if you do not know what you are doing. Attend a basic first aid course to learn the practice of first aid.

Principles of First Aid

First aid is emergency care for a person who is ill or injured, before medical help arrives. First aid is given to prevent death or to keep injuries from getting worse.

- Act quickly, giving priority to the most urgent conditions.

- Check that there is no further danger to the casualty or to yourself.

- If breathing has stopped, clear the airway and begin cardiopulmonary resuscitation.

- Control bleeding.

- Guard against shock.

- Give reassurance to the casualty and to onlookers.

- Position the casualty correctly.

- If you must move the casualty, immobilise fractures and dress large wounds.

- If needed, get the casualty to hospital for medical treatment as soon as possible.

- Observe carefully for any changes in the casualty's condition.

- Do not try to do too much yourself.

- Ensure that onlookers give you plenty of room.

- Do not give anything by mouth to a casualty who is unconscious or who may need an anaesthetic on arrival at hospital.

- Always record emergency incidents accurately and comprehensively in the prescribed format.

Recovery Position

The recovery position may be necessary to prevent the casualty from choking on the tongue or on vomit, especially if the person is unconscious and lying on his or her back.

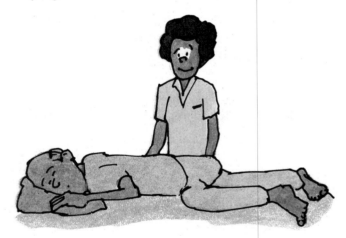

- Kneel beside the casualty, and place both of the person's arms close to the body.

- Turn the casualty onto the side.

- Draw the upper arm and leg upwards and outwards to form a right angle with the body. This prevents the person from rolling forward.

- Pull the underneath arm out gently behind the casualty. This will prevent rolling backwards.

Shock

All casualties experience a certain amount of shock. It is important for you to recognise the signs and symptoms of shock.

Signs and symptoms:

· The casualty feels sick, vomits, or may be thirsty.

· The skin is pale, cold, clammy, and may be sweating.

· Breathing becomes shallow and rapid with yawning and sighing.

· Pulse rate becomes quicker, but weaker.

· Unconsciousness may develop.

The treatment for shock aims at getting an adequate supply of blood to the brain and vital organs.

Treatment:

· Reassure the casualty.

· Lay the casualty down, and raise the legs if possible.

· Place in the recovery position if the person becomes unconscious.

· Keep the casualty warm.

· Loosen tight clothing to help circulation and breathing.

· Moisten the lips if the casualty is thirsty (but do not give anything to drink).

· Avoid moving the casualty unnecessarily.

· Begin cardiopulmonary resuscitation if breathing or heartbeat stops.

· Get the casualty to hospital as soon as possible (unless the casualty has simply fainted).

Burns and Scalds

Burns are generally caused by dry heat, electricity, friction, or corrosive chemicals. Scalds are caused by moist heat (e.g., boiling water).

The pain may be intense, especially with superficial burns. There is usually redness, and blistering occurs later. There is usually a great deal of shock.

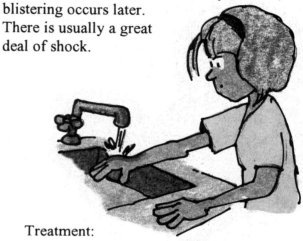

Treatment:

· Immerse the injured area in cold water or place under slowly running cold water for at least 10 minutes. This decreases the spread of heat and alleviates pain.

· Remove anything that constricts (e.g., rings, clothes, shoes) before the burned area begins to swell.

· Gently remove any clothing that has been soaked in boiling water. Burnt clothing has been sterilised and does not need to be removed.

· Lay the casualty down, and treat for shock.

· Cover the injured part with a clean, dry dressing.

· Give small amounts of cold drinks at frequent intervals if the person is conscious.

· Arrange for immediate removal to hospital for all but the most minor burns.

· Do not apply lotions or ointments.

· Do not prick blisters.

· Do not breathe over, cough over, or touch burned areas.

Bleeding

Major bleeding requires immediate treatment to save life. External bleeding is easy to see, but internal bleeding may only show itself as signs and symptoms of shock. The aim is to control the bleeding and to keep the wound free of infection.

Treatment:

· Uncover the wound and check for foreign objects. Do not touch any foreign object that is firmly embedded in a wound. Never pull out an object that has created a puncture wound (e.g., a knife).

· If there are no foreign bodies, apply direct pressure to the wound with the finger and/or hand, preferably over a sterile dressing.

· If the wound is large, squeeze the edges together to try to stop the bleeding.

· Lay the casualty down and treat for shock.

· If the wound is on a limb and there is no fracture, keep the limb raised.

· Place a sterile, unmedicated dressing over the wound and secure it firmly with a bandage.

· If the bleeding continues, apply additional dressings on top of the original dressing.

· If direct pressure does not stop the bleeding or if there is an embedded foreign body, use indirect pressure before continuing. To apply indirect pressure, press on the main artery that supplies blood to the limb, e.g., the brachial pressure point on the inside of the upper arm.

· Do not apply indirect pressure for more than 15 minutes at a time, and do not apply a tourniquet.

· Remove the person to hospital for treatment for all but the most minor cuts.

Choking

Clutching the throat is the universal sign for choking. When choking occurs, bend the person forward and give two or three hard slaps between the shoulder blades. Repeat if necessary. If the person is still choking, proceed with the Heimlich Manoeuvre.

Procedure for a conscious person:

1. Stand behind the person. Slide your arms under the choking person's arms and wrap them around the waist.

2. Make a fist and place it against the person's abdomen, below the rib cage and above the navel, being careful not to touch the sternum (centre breastbone).

3. Using your free hand, apply pressure against your fist with an inward and upward thrust.

4. Give four rapid thrusts, and repeat the procedure, if necessary. The abdominal thrusts dislodge the obstruction upwards and out from the airway so the person can spit it out.

Procedure for an unconscious person:

When a person loses consciousness from choking, the neck muscles may relax enough for the object to no longer completely obstruct the airway. You may be able to remove the obstruction by scooping it out with your fingers.

If the airway is still blocked:

1. Call for emergency help.

2. Place the casualty onto his or her back.

3. Open the airway by tilting the head back and lifting the chin.

4. Check for breathing.

5. If there is no breathing, open the mouth to see if you can scoop the obstruction out with your fingers.

6. Pinch the nose closed and ventilate (breathe air in) through the mouth with two full breaths.

7. If the airway is still blocked, kneel beside or straddle the person at hip level.

8. Place the heel of your hand on the person's abdomen below the rib cage with your fingers pointing toward the person's chest. Place your free hand over the positioned hand.

9. Position your shoulders over the casualty's abdomen, and thrust your hands inward and upward.

10. Give 6 to 10 rapid thrusts.

11. Check to see if the obstruction has been dislodged so that you can remove it from the mouth/throat.

12. Repeat steps 6 to 11, if necessary.

13. After the obstruction has been removed, if the person does not breathe, or if the heartbeat has stopped, start cardiopulmonary resuscitation.

Cardiopulmonary Resuscitation

Cardiopulmonary resuscitation (CPR) training teaches valuable lifesaving skills. The procedure uses mouth-to-mouth resuscitation and chest compression when the heart and/or the lungs have stopped working.

Quick action is critical. CPR must begin as soon as the heart stops in order to prevent brain and organ damage.

Only fully trained people should administer CPR. If you have not already attended a course on CPR, you should attend a class as soon as possible.

The following information is **NOT** a CPR course. It is intended as a basic review for those who have completed CPR training.

1. Call for help.

2. Shake the victim (unless actual or possible injuries prevent you from doing so), and call the casualty's name.

3. If there is no response, check for breathing.

   · **Look** for chest movements.

   · **Listen** by putting your ear near the casualty's nose and mouth.

   · **Feel** for breath on your cheek.

4. If there is no breathing, begin artificial respiration (you artificially breathe for the person).

5. Use precautions to prevent infection, if possible. (Remember, you are potentially at-risk from all people.)

6. Tilt the head back by lifting the neck.

7. Pinch the nose closed to prevent air from escaping from the nostrils, and cover the casualty's mouth completely with your mouth.

8. Blow into the person's mouth until you see the chest rise. Blow two breaths and then turn your head to the side to listen for air.

9. Check the carotid pulse at the side of the neck. If there is no pulse, begin to artificially pump the casualty's heart.

   · Ensure that the casualty is lying on a firm surface.

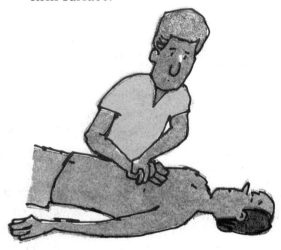

   · Locate the lower end of the sternum and place the heel of the hand over the end portion of the casualty's sternum.

   · Then place the heel of your other hand over the top of the first hand to increase leverage.

   · Use the heels of your hands to compress the chest 15 times.

10. Continue to give two breaths followed by 15 chest compressions until medical help arrives.

If there are two people available from the outset, they should work together. One person does the mouth-to-mouth and the other person does the chest compressions. The requirement here is for one breath to five chest compressions.

Diabetes Mellitus

Diabetes Mellitus is a medical condition where a person cannot produce enough insulin. Insulin is the hormone produced by the pancreas to help the body break down and convert sugars and starches into energy. Two complications of diabetes which require prompt attention are hyperglycaemia and hypoglycaemia.

Diabetic coma (hyperglycaemia) is the result of too little insulin or too much sugar. It occurs when blood sugar levels are high and there is an acidosis due to ketones being present in the blood. Although the onset of this condition is gradual, it is life-threatening and requires immediate care.

Early signs of hyperglycaemia:

· increased urination

· abdominal pain

· nausea

· drowsiness

· thirst

Later signs of hyperglycaemia:

· heavy breathing

· breath smells of pear drops

· flushed face

· dry skin

· loss of consciousness

Stay with the person to offer reassurance until the ambulance arrives to take him or her to hospital for treatment. Make sure that you inform all relevant people that the person has been taken to hospital.

At hospital, insulin is given to reduce the blood sugar and sodium bicarbonate solution (an alkali) is given to counteract acidosis and dehydration.

Insulin shock (hypoglycaemia) is the result of too much insulin or too little sugar. The onset of this condition is very quick as the lowered blood sugar affects the functioning of the brain.

Signs of hypoglycaemia are:

- lethargy, weakness, dizziness

- confusion or bad temperedness

- hunger

- sweating

- trembling

- unconsciousness

Treatment includes giving glucose orally, as quickly as possible, before the person loses consciousness. In severe cases where the person has lost consciousness, glucose is injected intravenously (into a vein) by a doctor.

Stay with the person, and offer reassurance until he or she recovers. This should happen very quickly after the glucose has been administered.

Report hypoglycaemic attacks to the person in charge, and accurately record the details of the attack (date, time, symptoms, speed of recovery, etc.).

If you are unsure whether a person who has Diabetes Mellitus is having a hypoglycaemic or a hyperglycaemic attack, give the person glucose. If it is hypoglycaemia, recovery will happen very quickly. If it is hyperglycaemia, no harm will be done because it is the acidosis in hyperglycaemia that causes the major problems, not the raised blood sugar.

Seizures

A seizure (fit) occurs when normal brain cell activity is interrupted by abnormal discharges of electricity within the brain. Seizures can happen to anyone. They are often caused by:

- tumours

- head injury

- infection and fever

- chemical imbalance

- stroke

Sometimes no cause can be found. When a person tends to have repeated seizures, even rarely, the person is said to have epilepsy.

The main treatment for epilepsy is medication. Medication strengthens a person's resistance to seizures. It is important that people who suffer from epilepsy take their medication regularly, as prescribed. Medication completely controls epilepsy for some people; for others, seizures are kept to a minimum.

Generalised absence (petit mal) seizures are characterised by the person looking blank and staring. There may be slight blinking or twitching. This type of seizure lasts only for a few seconds. Afterward, the person continues as normal, as if nothing has happened, unaware of the seizure.

Complex partial (psychomotor) seizures may start with an "aura" or warning (e.g., seeing flashing lights or having a horrible taste in the mouth). The person appears confused or distracted and may repeat a series of movements (e.g., plucking at clothes).

Generalised tonic-clonic (grand mal) seizures tend to have a common sequence of events. However, not every tonic-clonic seizure will exactly follow the sequence. There may be an aura followed by staring, followed by a stiffening of the body, which usually results in the person falling to the ground. The person may cry out. There may be a blue colour around the mouth and extremities.

Eventually the person commences convulsions (jerking movements). As these fade away, breathing restarts, and normal colour returns. There is often foaming at the mouth, and this can be blood-flecked. Occasionally, there is incontinence. The person may appear to sleep for a short while before regaining consciousness.

This type of seizure can last for several minutes. It tends to be noisy and appears very frightening to onlookers.

Status epilepticus occurs when a person has repeated tonic-clonic seizures without recovering consciousness. This is an emergency. The person may die if he or she does not receive medical attention quickly.

> Do whatever is necessary to protect the person from injury during a seizure. Do not try to restrain the person. Never pry the mouth open, and do not insert anything into the mouth.

Care for Tonic-Clonic Seizure:

- Call for help and do whatever is necessary to protect the person from injury.

- Try to catch the person before he or she falls to the floor. If the person has not fallen to the floor, lie the person down.

- Move furniture and equipment out of the way to prevent injury during the convulsion stage of the seizure.

- If the person is in bed and there are side rails, pad them with blankets or soft foam.

- Take care to protect the head from injury during the seizure.

- Do not leave the person alone during the seizure

- If possible, turn the head to one side to prevent choking.

After a tonic-clonic seizure be aware that the person will not remember the seizure. Reassure the person. Help the person to his or her feet.

If the seizure occurs in a care facility, follow these guidelines:

- Help the person to bed.

- Report all seizures to the person in charge.

- Chart the seizure, recording all relevant details (date, time, description of the seizure, length of recovery, etc.).

- Observe closely in case the person is confused or has another seizure.

Electrocution

Electrical injuries can kill or cause a wide range of injuries, including severe burns and heart stoppage. Most electrical accidents involve household appliances, but lightning has the same effect.

The extent of injuries usually depends on the strength of the electrical current, how long the victim was exposed, and amount of insulation (e.g., whether the victim was wearing rubber-soled shoes or standing on a dry surface).

Never approach the victim of an electrical accident until you are sure it is safe. If the casualty is still in contact with the source of electricity, cut off the power supply before you touch the person by turning off the switch or unplugging the appliance.

If you cannot turn off the electricity supply because there are high voltage power lines, do not approach. You can receive a fatal shock up to 20 yards away. If it is household equipment that you cannot turn off and the casualty is still holding the source of electricity, stand on a rubber mat or dry newspaper, and lever the person's hand away using a wooden broom handle.

Once the casualty is safely removed from the electrical source, you can apply first aid. Smother any flames with a blanket or towel. If the casualty has been thrown to the ground by the electrical shock, check for breathing and pulse. Start CPR if necessary. Then check that there are no fractures, and treat any burns. Electrical burns may be much deeper than their size suggests. Provide reassurance and help as needed.

Chest Pains

Chest pains can occur for a number of reasons. The most common cause of chest pain is angina. Angina is a severe, but temporary, attack of chest pain which is often induced by exercise. A person with chest pains will have a good idea whether the pain is angina or not. If it is angina, sit or lay the person down and help him or her to take a heart tablet that angina sufferers always have with them. The tablet is placed under the tongue and allowed to dissolve. At rest, the angina attack should soon disappear.

Chest pain could signal a heart attack. A heart attack is a potentially fatal reduction in blood supply to the heart. Be alert to any signs of a heart attack:

- severe shock
- severe and constricting pain in the chest, sometimes radiating down the left arm and left side of the neck
- shortness of breath
- weak and irregular pulse
- unconsciousness

First Aid for a Heart Attack:

- Provide reassurance.
- Put the casualty into the most comfortable position. This might be sitting up, as that is the best position to help breathing.
- Loosen tight clothing at neck, chest, and waist, and encourage deep breathing.
- Get medical attention as quickly as possible as the casualty will need urgent treatment.
- If the casualty becomes unconscious, check the pulse and respirations. Commence CPR if there is no pulse or respiration.

Fractures

A fracture is a cracked or broken bone. There are two main causes of fracture:

- direct force (e.g., from a kick to the shin)

- indirect force (e.g., falling on an outstretched hand and fracturing the collar bone)

The casualty may have heard the bone break. Crepitus (the sound of two broken ends of bone grating together) can sometimes be heard. The casualty will probably not be able to use the affected part of the body, or it will be very painful to do so. The area of skin over the fracture will usually be swollen and bruised. The body part may be in an unnatural position or look different than the same body part on the other side of the body.

Closed fracture

The skin is unbroken, although there may be heavy bruising. This type of fracture can be **simple** when there is little damage to surrounding tissues. It can be **complicated** when there is damage to surrounding tissues, e.g., when a fractured pelvis punctures the bladder.

Compound fracture

The bone protrudes through the skin, or the skin is lacerated above the fracture leaving an opening for micro-organisms to enter.

Greenstick fracture

The bone is bent and may half break. These fractures occur in children.

First Aid for Fractures

Treat all bone injuries as fractures until diagnosis proves otherwise. Move the casualty as little as possible. Make the casualty as comfortable as possible, using great care so that you do not increase pain and shock.

Gently remove clothing from any open wound over the break, and cover with a clean dressing. If a bone protrudes, pack round it so that the bandage used to hold the dressing does not press directly onto the bone.

Immobilise the fracture if possible. There are many different ways of immobilising fractures. For example, put a broken arm in a sling or immobilise a broken leg by using the other leg as a splint, not forgetting to pad between boney prominences.

Treat for shock and provide reassurance. Get the casualty to hospital as quickly as possible. Do not give anything to eat or drink.

Exercise

When next you are present at a medical emergency, assess how well the incident is handled by the people managing the emergency. If you are involved in managing the emergency, assess how well you coped. Were you confident? How did you feel during the emergency?

Write a report of the incident for discussion with your NVQ/SVQ Assessor. Include the report in your portfolio.

Check Your Knowledge and Understanding

1. Which of the following is not one of the key areas for action in the Health of the Nation White Paper?

   a) neonatal deaths

   b) cancers

   c) accidents

   d) HIV/AIDS and sexual health

2. You smell burning at work one day, although you cannot see a fire or any smoke.

   What would you do?

   a) Ignore the smell of burning as it may be coming from outside the building.

   b) Carry out a more thorough search for the source of the smell.

   c) Immediately raise the alarm and evacuate the building.

   d) Walk around the building to check that the fire extinguishers are all in working order.

3. You need to move a person up in bed. Another carer, who comes to help you lift, states that she does not like the shoulder lift and cannot do it properly. She proposes that you do the ''drag lift,'' a non-authorised lift.

What would you do?

   a) Go ahead and use the drag lift because there is nobody else available to help you at the moment.

   b) Insist that the other member of staff attempts the shoulder lift with you.

   c) Lift the person up in bed by yourself.

   d) Gently explain that you would prefer to do the shoulder lift; and, therefore, you will wait until somebody else is available to help you.

4. An intravenous drug user, who is known to be HIV positive, is attending your day centre. Several of your colleagues claim that they are scared of catching AIDS.

   What would you do?

   a) Say, ''I can understand your fears, but there is nothing you can do to stop this person attending the day centre.''

   b) Suggest that your colleagues book in for an AIDS workshop.

   c) Advise them to see the day centre manager to express their fears and pick up copies of the AIDS leaflets.

   d) Tell them to stop being silly as they cannot catch AIDS from this person unless they have intimate sexual contact.

5. Someone comes to you who has just sustained a nasty burn on his hand from touching the steam iron.

   What would you do?

   a) Immediately apply a clean, dry dressing to prevent infection, after removing the person's rings in case the fingers blister.

   b) Immediately apply some antiseptic cream after removing the rings, but before you apply the dressing.

   c) Immediately put this person's hand under a slow-running cold tap, and gently slip the rings off the person's finger.

   d) Prick the blisters as they start to form, and then apply a clean dry dressing.

6. A diabetic client, who is suffering from an ear infection, claims to be feeling unwell. He appears to be a bit confused and is sweating.

   What would you do?

   a) Quickly put a couple of glucose sweets into the person's mouth.

   b) Call for the doctor.

   c) Ask him to go to bed, and offer him an aspirin, saying that you will check up on him later to see if he is any better.

   d) Advise the client to give himself more insulin.

See page 124 for answers.

Tips On Evidence Collection

1. Include in your portfolio all the work that you completed during the module exercises.

2. Include details in your portfolio if you attend any training sessions on safe lifting technique, infection control, first aid, fire safety, etc.

3. Obtain copies of any policies pertaining to health and safety, health promotion, security, etc., and keep them in your portfolio.

Module 7 References

Department of Employment (1974) **Health and Safety at Work Act**. HMSO: London.

Department of Health and Social Security (1968) **Public Health (Infectious Diseases) Regulations**. HMSO: London.

Department of Health and Social Security(1986) **The Health of the Nation**. HMSO: London.

Department of Trade and Industry (1988) **The Control of Substances Hazardous to Health Regulations**. HMSO: London.

Medical Council on Alcoholism (1990) **Alcohol and Health: A Handbook for Nurses, Midwives and Health Visitors**. MCA: London.

World Health Organisation (1948) **The World Health Organisation Constitution**. WHO: Copenhagen.

Module 8

Handling Information About Care

Unit U5

- a core unit for both the Level 2 and Level 3 NVQ/SVQ Award in Care

Unit U5 is primarily concerned with obtaining, transmitting, and storing information related to the delivery of care, according to relevant legislation and organisational policies.

The care team depend on your accurate and timely information to manage each person's care.

Objectives:

- ☐ Outline how information should be collected.
- ☐ Explain the importance of observation skills.
- ☐ Describe how to record information on charts and records.
- ☐ Discuss how to maintain records according to organisational policies.
- ☐ Outline the ways that data can be protected.
- ☐ Explain the difference between objective and subjective reporting.
- ☐ Describe how to receive and transmit messages.

Module 8 Glossary

data	accumulated information or facts	oedema	abnormal swelling of the tissues due to retention of fluid
hives	rash similar to that caused by nettles	tranquilliser	drug that has a sedative and calming effect
lethargy	a state of listlessness and lack of energy		

Art

Part 1	**Obtaining Information** *(U5.a)*

Your observations provide important information for the care team.

An important part of your role is obtaining information. You need to be very careful that you pass on accurate and timely information and maintain confidentiality.

Information about care services often needs to be obtained from people receiving care, their families, and from other care workers. Follow these guidelines for obtaining information:

- Be sure that your request for information is appropriate.

- Be clear about the information you need and the timescale within which you need it.

- Allow time for the person to respond.

- When necessary, confirm the relevance and accuracy of information. Check that the information is up-to-date and seek further information as needed.

- Always safeguard confidential information.

Gathering information requires varying degrees of detail. If a person is being admitted for care, you may have to collect personal details such as name, address, date of birth, etc. If the person cannot provide details of nonessential information at the time of admission obtain the details later. For example, if the person forgets the post code, you can obtain the information later.

Information must be accurate and thorough. For example, if the information pertains to child abuse, double check details for accuracy. The information may be necessary for use in court. It is important to check the currency, accuracy, and relevance of information. For example, it is no good sending an appointment to an address if the person no longer lives there.

Another example is when a patient is sent to the operating theatre. The patient wears a wrist band that identifies the person and contains a unique hospital number. The band ensures that the person is not given the wrong operation. It is essential to check that you have the correct patient. If the name and number on the patient's wrist band do not match those on the operating theatre list, double check before admitting the person to theatre.

Observing

Being a skilled observer helps prevent serious problems and earns the respect of your colleagues. Being alert to people and their environment helps to reduce accidents and maintain the well-being of the people in your care.

Careful observations increase your awareness of each person's physical, emotional, and social needs. Learn to recognise signs and symptoms of common diseases and conditions. One of your major roles in providing care is to detect problems in their early stages.

Trust your instincts. If something appears to be wrong, report it. Any physical or emotional changes may indicate a change in the condition of the person's health.

Be alert to physical changes:

- decreased or increased functioning (e.g., elimination, pulse, breathing)
- unconscious, weak, trembling
- drowsy, lethargic
- cold, pale, clammy
- hot, sweating, burning, feverish
- nausea, vomiting
- diarrhoea, constipation
- excessive thirst
- odour
- ringing in ears
- blurred vision
- spasms
- pain, difficulty, discomfort
- swelling, oedema
- rash, hives, blisters
- choking, coughing, wheezing, sneezing

> **Observe each person throughout your daily contacts.**
>
> **WATCH   LOOK   LISTEN**

Be alert to emotional changes:

- mood swings, loss of control
- depressed, helpless, crying, tearful
- angry, difficult, irrational
- disoriented, confused
- anxious, frightened, pacing

Charting

The chart is a person's written health record. It is a legal document. Accuracy is very important.

Follow these guidelines to record on a person's chart/record:

- Ensure that you complete only the records or charts for which you have been given responsibility.
- Where necessary, write your notes out on a piece of paper first to check the accuracy, spelling, and grammar, before entering your notes on the record.

- Write neatly and clearly in ink.

- Correct errors by drawing a single line through the error and signing it. Never erase or "white out" a record.

- Always date and time your record as appropriate.

- Record only procedures that you have done, after they are done.

- Do not forget to record any relevant information.

- Always sign your record entry.

- Keep all information confidential.

If you have any worries or uncertainties about managing information, seek advice.

Part 2	**Handling Records** (U5.b)

Maintaining accurate records helps plan care.

Records are important documents in the form of paperwork or electronic data. Be sure to update records accurately and to store them safely so that the records can be retrieved and used at a later date.

Confidential records should be marked as such and must be safely stored when not in use. Confidential records held on computer should be guarded by an access code so that only people with the correct code can gain access to the information.

Maintaining Records

To complete or update records, identify that you have the correct records. Be careful to enter only accurate data; inaccurate information can be illegal and dangerous.

Tracking Records

Make a note when records are transferred to other locations. Identify where the records were sent so that they can be traced if necessary.

Following Organisation Policies

Make sure that you know organisation policies relating to confidentiality, access, and transmission of information that pertain to your role. This includes knowing the records that can be accessed by people receiving care and those to which they should not have access. For example, it is appropriate that a person should have access to his or her own medical records, but not to budget sheets or the accident book for a particular establishment.

Inform your manager if your part of the organisation maintains, stores, and retrieves records in a way that appears to conflict with good practice. For example, in a busy department, it is easy to leave confidential records lying around where they can be illegally accessed. If you need advice, contact the nominated Information Officer for your organisation.

Data Protection Act (1984) establishes requirements for electronically-held information. Personal data must meet these requirements:

- obtained fairly and lawfully

- held only for lawful purposes, as specified in the act

- adequate, relevant, and not excessive for the specified purposes

- accurate and, where necessary, up-to-date

- kept no longer than necessary for the specified purposes

- made available to the person upon request

- properly protected against loss or disclosure

Part 3   Receiving Information and Providing It To Others *(U5.c)*

Provide accurate information about the people in your care.

Thorough and accurate reports are made to your colleagues as often as a person's condition requires. End-of-shift and staff meeting reports provide information necessary for the planning of continued quality care.

Correct:	Mrs. Jones said her left ear aches.
Correct:	Mrs. Jones' left leg is red, swollen, and warm to the touch.

Reporting

Reports should include the person's name, detailed description of your observations, and other relevant information.

Objective reporting means to report precisely what you saw, smelled, felt, or heard. If a person complains of symptoms that you cannot observe or measure (e.g., dizziness or pain), report exactly what the person told you.

Subjective reporting is used to report what you cannot sense or measure. When possible, avoid using subjective reporting. However, if you think there is something wrong, medically or emotionally, you must report it.

Incorrect:	Mrs. Jones has an ear infection.
Correct:	Mrs. Jones is holding her hand up to the right side of her face and seems very uncomfortable.

Transmitting Information

Receiving and transmitting information is an essential part of quality care. Accurate information is necessary in order to avoid mistakes or misunderstandings.

Before providing information, politely check the person's identity. Also check whether that person has right of access to the information. Do not be afraid to refuse to give information if you are not sure that the person has right of access. If the person has right of access, but you do not have the requested information, quickly find out where the person can access the information. Refer the person to the appropriate place.

Always require proof of identity. Since identity cannot be checked over the telephone, never provide confidential information over the telephone. You can easily check proof of identity for health and social services staff by asking to look at identity cards. All staff should carry identity cards, whether they wear uniforms or not.

Receiving Messages

Ask callers to write down and leave their own messages where possible. If this is not possible (e.g., the person is in a hurry or the person cannot write), write down the message immediately so that you do not forget it. Use the prescribed message slips if available. Read the message to check with the person for accuracy and clarity.

All telephone messages should be written down. Write the message during the phone call or immediately afterwards so that you do not forget the details. Use prescribed message slips if available. Read the message to the person to check for clarity and accuracy.

All messages should include the following information:

- name of the person who is sending the message

- name of the person who is to receive the message

- signature of the person passing on the message

- date and time the message was received

- date and time the message was given

- clear details of the communicated message

- indication of urgency

- whether it was a verbal or a telephone message

Choose an appropriate method to transmit messages, e.g., telephone, internal post, or word of mouth. Get the information to the target person within a reasonable time, depending on the urgency of the message. Do not be afraid to disturb a member of staff in a meeting if the message is urgent. If in doubt about the urgency of a message, seek advice.

Check the identity of the person to whom you are delivering the message. If necessary, explain the message so that the person understands what it means.

If you hand on the message to another person for delivery, ensure that the person understands the urgency of the message. Make sure the message is in an envelope marked ''confidential'' if it contains confidential information.

If delivering the message over the telephone and the person is not available, do not leave a verbal message if you are concerned about confidentiality. Simply leave your name and telephone number so that the person can contact you.

Exercise

Assess the way information is managed by your part of the organisation. Write notes under the following headings:

· quality of charts and client records

· availability and clarity of policies governing data protection and data management

· ways that confidentiality is maintained for paper and electronic records

· appropriateness of methods used for receiving and transmitting messages

Write a report on your assessment of the way that information is managed within your organisation. Highlight both good and bad practices that you observed. Discuss the report with your manager and/or your NVQ/SVQ Assessor.

Check Your Knowledge and Understanding

1. You notice that Jane, a person in your care, has severe abrasions to the outside of her left arm. She refuses to tell you how it happened. Jane has a past history of self-injury, including scraping her arms against the wall while walking down the street.

   What would be the most accurate way that you could report this in her care record?

   a) "Jane has been scraping her arm along the wall again, resulting in some severe abrasions to her left arm."

   b) "Jane has severe abrasions on her left arm. It looks as though she has started injuring herself again."

   c) "Jane has severe abrasions to her left arm. She refuses to say how this happened."

   d) "Jane has hurt her left arm. It is not known how this happened."

2. You are writing in the care record. You notice that you have made a mistake. In your haste, you have written in the wrong person's record.

   What would you do?

   a) Put a single line through the mistake and sign it.

   b) "White out" the mistake with correction fluid, and then commence writing on the correct record sheet.

   c) Tear out the sheet of paper on which the mistake was made, re-writing all the previous records that were written on the sheet.

   d) Scribble out your mistake, and commence writing on the correct record sheet.

3. You are using the client database to access a client record for a forthcoming case conference. Your access code does not allow you to access a relevant report on this client from a Child Protection Officer.

   What would you do?

   a) Access the computers hard-disk maintenance system, trying to bypass the protection on the child protection report.

   b) Ask to borrow a colleague's access code to access the report that you need.

   c) Contact the Child Protection Officer to send you a copy of the report through the post.

   d) Inform your manager that you cannot access the child protection report. Someone else will have to access that report to have it available for the case conference.

4. A message comes through to your office that a colleague's daughter has been injured at school and admitted to hospital. Your colleague is going to be in a case conference for the next hour or more.

   What would you do?

   a) Write the message on the whiteboard so that your colleague will see it.

   b) Interrupt the case conference immediately and ask your colleague to come out so that you can give him the message.

   c) Write out the message and leave it on your colleague's desk or in-tray.

   d) Inform your colleague as soon as he leaves the case conference.

5. An elderly and disabled lady, who lives alone in her own house in the community, phones to inform the community nurse that she has run out of tranquilliser tablets. The nurse is out on her rounds and will be returning at lunch time.

   What would you do?

   a) Write the message on a message slip, and leave it on the nurse's desk.

   b) Try to contact the nurse immediately by phoning all the patients she is due to visit that morning.

   c) Verbally pass on the message to the nurse when she arrives at lunchtime, if you see her.

   d) Pass the message on to one of the nurse's colleagues so that she can deliver it.

6. A "social worker" arrives at your residential home, wanting to interview one of the residents and have access to the resident's case notes. Nobody at the home knows this social worker, and the person carries no identification.

   What would you do?

   a) Accept the social worker's word, and allow her access to the resident and the resident's case notes.

   b) Tell the social worker to go away and not to come back until she has some identification.

c) Phone the Social Services Department and ask for a description of the social worker to confirm identity.

d) Allow the social worker access to the resident, but not the records. Then make a formal complaint to the Social Services Department about the social worker not having any identification.

See page 124 for answers.

Tips On Evidence Collection

1. If there is any legislation covering your area of work, include relevant details in your portfolio (e.g., Access to Health Records Act, Access to Personal Files Regulations, Data Protection Act).

2. If you experience problems in managing information, write up how you dealt with it for inclusion in your portfolio.

3. If you attend a course or workshop on information management or computer skills, include programme details in your portfolio.

Module 8 References

Department of Health (1990) **Access to Health Records Act**. HMSO: London.

Department of Health and Social Security (1989) **Access to Personal Files (Social Services) Regulations**. HMSO: London.

Department of Trade and Industry (1984) **Data Protection Act**. HMSO: London.

References

Brearley G & Birchley P (1986) **Introducing Counselling Skills and Techniques.** Faber & Faber: London.

Byrne T & Padfield C F (1985) **Social Services: Made Simple.** Heinemann: London.

Department of Employment (1974) **Health and Safety at Work Act.** HMSO: London.

Department of Health (1990) **HIV: the Causitive Agent of AIDS and Related Conditions. Second Revision of Guidelines by the Advisory Committee on Dangerous Pathogens.** HMSO: London.

Department of Health (1990) **Access to Health Records Act.** HMSO: London.

Department of Health (1990) **National Health Service and Community Care Act.** HMSO: London.

Department of Health (1990) **Code of Practice: Mental Health Act 1993.** HMSO: London.

Department of Health (1991) **The Patient's Charter.** HMSO: London.

Department of Health (1992) **Report of the Committee of Enquiry into Complaints about Ashworth Hospital.** HMSO: London.

Department of Health and Social Security (1933) **The Children and Young Persons Act.** HMSO: London.

Department of Health and Social Security (1968) **Public Health (Infectious Diseases) Regulations.** HMSO: London.

Department of Health and Social Security (1983) **Mental Health Act.** HMSO: London.

Department of Health and Social Security(1986) **The Health of the Nation.** HMSO: London.

Department of Health and Social Security (1988) **Advisory Committee Report: Violence to Staff.** HMSO: London.

Department of Health and Social Security (1989) **Access to Personal Files (Social Services) Regulations.** HMSO: London.

Department of Trade and Industry (1984) **Data Protection Act.** HMSO: London.

Department of Trade and Industry (1988) **The Control of Substances Hazardous to Health Regulations.** HMSO: London.

Dingwall R (1984) **Who is to blame anyway?** Nursing Times, April 11, 42-43.

Equal Opportunities Commission (1986) **Guidelines for Equal Opportunities Employers.** EOC: London.

Farrell G A & Gray C (1992) **Aggression: A Nurse's Guide to Therapeutic Management.** Scutari Press: London.

Health and Safety Commission (1987) **Violence to Staff in the Health Services.** HMSO: London.

Ironbar N O & Hooper A (1989) **Self-Instruction in Mental Health Nursing.** Balliere Tindall: London.

Kagan C et al (1986) **A Manual of Interpersonal Skills for Nurses: An Experiential Approach.** Harper & Row: London.

Kubler-Ross E (1969) **On Death and Dying.** MacMillan: New York.

Medical Council on Alcoholism (1990) **Alcohol and Health: A Handbook for Nurses, Midwives and Health Visitors.** MCA: London.

O'Kell S P (1993) **Managing Organisational Stress, part 1.** Senior Nurse, 13, 3, 9-13.

Parry G (1990) **Coping with Crises.** Routledge Ltd: London.

Poyner B & Warne C (1988) **Health and Safety Executive Report: Preventing Violence to Staff.** HMSO: London.

Tschudin V (1989) **Beginning with Empathy: A Learner's Handbook.** Churchill Livingstone: New York.

United Kingdom Central Council for Nursing, Midwifery and Health Visiting (1987) **Confidentiality: an Elaboration of Clause 9.** UKCC: London.

United Kingdom Central Council for Nursing, Midwifery and Health Visiting (1992) **The Scope of Professional Practice.** UKCC: London.

United Nations (1948) **Universal Declaration of Human Rights.** UN: Geneva.

United Nations (1971) **Declaration on the Rights of Mentally Retarded Persons.** UN: Geneva.

Wondrak R (1989) **Dealing with Verbal Abuse.** Nurse Education Today, 9, 276-280.

World Health Organisation (1948) **The World Health Organisation Constitution.** WHO: Copenhagen.

Answers to Check Your Knowledge and Understanding

Module 1
pages 18-19

Question 1   Answer: **b**

Explanation: It should not be your decision to break the rules of confidentiality in this case. The person-in-charge will probably decide to inform the Child Protection Officer. He or she might also want to interview the parent first and inform the parent of the intentions.

Question 2   Answer: **c**

Explanation: It is best to let the nurse-in-charge deal with this request. A patient can compel the release of computerised medical records, unless it can be contested that sight of the records could be harmful to the patient. But, most hospitals have policies to deal with this situation. Policies can include the expectation that at least two days' notice is needed before a copy of medical records is provided and there may be a charge levied for the service.

Question 3   Answer: **d**

Explanation: You have tried to politely stop this man from harassing you. It has not worked. Therefore, it is time to take this problem further and get it sorted out.

Question 4   Answer: **c**

Explanation: Dehumanisation is an **effect** of institutionalisation on the individual, not a characteristic of institutionalisation.

Question 5   Answers: **a and b**

Explanation: The needs of the person contemplating suicide and the needs of the abused child override the need to maintain confidentiality.

Question 6   Answer: **c**

Explanation: This is the only logical alternative that will meet this man's needs to fast and your need to ensure that he consumes a good diet in order to regain some of the weight that he has lost.

Module 2
pages 29-30

Question 1   Answer: **all**

Explanation: All are causes of challenging behaviour.

Question 2   Answer: **b**

Explanation: A reprimand is likely to escalate, rather than de-escalate the situation.

Question 3   Answers: **b and d**

Explanation: Answer ''b'' is a physical symptom linked to many other illnesses. Answer ''d'' is a sign of psychological, rather than physical abuse.

Question 4   Answer: **d**

Explanation: Significant others are part of the care environment.

Question 5   Answer: **a**

Explanation: A clear, concise, and accurate objective report should be immediately written while the incident is still fresh in the memory.

Question 6   Answer: **c**

Explanation: If the person is only at slight risk from abuse, it is a waste of staff time to maintain constant supervision (especially if the person could be at-risk for the rest of his life).

Module 3
pages 40-41

Question 1 Answer: **c**

Explanation: Given the potential danger of the assault and that you first attempted to use minimum force with no effect, you have committed no crime. The injury sustained by John is incidental because you used the minimum force necessary to stop the assault.

Question 2 Answer: **a**

Explanation: Once outside, Fred was not a danger to anybody. Losing buttons from your shirt did not warrant your extra action of pushing him away. You have clearly assaulted Fred.

Question 3 Answer: **a**

Explanation: May should have mentioned that she did not want a bath. She had no good reason for slapping you. She has clearly assaulted you. But, May had stopped the assault and was not threatening you before you slapped her. You are, therefore, guilty of assault.

Question 4 Answer: **c**

Explanation: The man has a reason to be upset because he has been kept waiting. It is important not only to apologise, but also to acknowledge what the person might be thinking/feeling. This defuses the situation by ensuring the man does not feel ignored while ensuring that his need for food is met.

Question 5 Answer: **c**

Explanation: With this answer, you are responding to the woman's wish to be left alone while leaving an opening for a later meeting.

Question 6 Answer: **b**

Explanation: You do not know this man, and you do not know how he will react to you. If you enlist the help of someone who does know him well, the person is more likely to be able to choose the appropriate action to take.

Module 4
pages 51-52

Question 1 Answer: **all**

Explanation: They are all communication problems.

Question 2 Answer: **d**

Explanation: The only thing that matters is that when the lady is discharged, she takes her medication as prescribed and attends the day centre. Answer "d" is most likely to get that result.

Question 3 Answer: **c**

Explanation: Conception occurs at the moment a woman becomes pregnant.

Question 4 Answers: **b and c**

Explanation: Answer "b" is incorrect because nobody should be forced to use any language they do not feel comfortable using. Answer "c" is wrong because pressure should not be put on a person to talk about his problems when he is not yet ready to talk about them.

Question 5 Answer: **a**

Explanation: Never shout at anybody.

Question 6 Answers: **a and c**

Explanation: Answer "b" is inappropriate for spectacles that have plastic lenses. Answer "d" is inappropriate because you should not always encourage people to use a neck strap. Some people do not like neck straps, and some people do not need them .

Module 5   pages 63-64

Question 1   Answer: **b**

Explanation: Relaxation techniques are easy to learn and would allow the friend to get on with his life.

Question 2   Answer: **all**

Explanation: They are all stages of grief.

Question 3   Answer: **b**

Explanation: This is restating (repeating the ideas of the client in your own words).

Question 4   Answer: **a and d**

Explanation: Neither depression nor anger are essential features of a crisis.

Question 5   Answer: **all**

Explanation: They are all incorrect. a) Stress stimulates the sympathetic nervous system. b) Stress is unavoidable. c) Performance improves with increasing stress only until the optimum level of arousal is reached and from then on performance decreases. d) A traffic jam is a minor stressor.

Question 6   Answer: **a**

Explanation: Relaxation and exercise are not major categories of help that is provided to people in crisis. The last thing that most people in a crisis want is exercise.

Module 6   pages 73-74

Question 1   Answer: **all**

Explanation: All of them are significant reasons why resources will not stretch to meet everybody's needs in the public sector services.

Question 2   Answer: **a**

Explanation: You are bound by the rules of confidentiality in answers "b" and "c". In answer "d", you are leaving yourself open to allegations of fraud and deception.

Question 3   Answer: **a**

Explanation: Welfare benefits offices are usually well-situated, near to the centre of towns.

Question 4   Answers: **a and c**

Explanation: Answer "a" causes dependence and/or laziness. In Answer "c" the information may be incorrect.

Question 5   Answers: **b and d**

Explanation: In answer "b", risks can be taken as long as they have been assessed by the multidisciplinary team as being appropriate. In answer "d", a person has the right to have personal information kept confidential (even from family).

Question 6   Answer: **b**

Explanation: They are all domiciliary services.

Module 7
pages 109-110

Question 1   Answer: **a**

Explanation: Neonatal deaths are not a major area of concern within the United Kingdom at this time.

Question 2   Answer: **c**

Explanation: Answer ''c'' is the only safe alternative. Just because you cannot see flames or smoke does not mean that there is not a fire. The fire brigade would rather be called out to a fire at this stage than to a blazing inferno. They will not be angry if it is a false alarm.

Question 3   Answer: **d**

Explanation: Answer ''d'' is the only option. Answers ''a'', and ''c'' are lifts where you are likely to hurt yourself and/or the person receiving care. Answer ''b'' is not appropriate if the other member of staff cannot do the lift. You should inform your manager about the member of staff who cannot use the prescribed lifts.

Question 4   Answer: **c**

Explanation: Answer ''c'' is the most appropriate answer. Answer ''b'' is second best because it may be quite awhile before these people can be released for the AIDS workshop. Answer ''a'' is simply an unhelpful comment. Answer ''d'' is incorrect.

Question 5   Answer: **c**

Explanation: Answer ''c'' is the correct, immediate, first aid treatment for a burn.

Question 6   Answer: **a**

Explanation: If the person is hypoglycaemic as you suspect, the sweets will allow him to recover quickly. If the person does not quickly recover, call the doctor. All the other options are highly dangerous.

Module 8
pages 117-119

Question 1   Answer: **c**

Explanation: Answer ''c'' is an accurate, objective report. Answers ''a'' and ''b'' make assumptions that Jane is injuring herself again when there is no proof. Answer ''d'' is not a full report of what you know.

Question 2   Answer: **a**

Explanation: This is the only way to rectify a written mistake in a person's care record.

Question 3   Answer: **d**

Explanation: You are obviously not allowed access to this report, so you should not try to access it by other means.

Question 4   Answer: **b**

Explanation: The message is urgent. You should pass the message on to your colleague as quickly and gently as possible.

Question 5   Answer: **a**

Explanation: The message is not urgent, although it is important that the nurse receives the message that day to ensure that the patient gets another supply of tablets that day. The nurse will check her desk for messages so there is no danger that she will not receive the message.

Question 6   Answer: **c**

Explanation: It makes sense not to allow anybody access to the home, never mind the residents and records, until there is proof of identification. Simply sending the social worker away would appear to be unfriendly when you can call the Social Services Department for proof of identity.

Multiple Choice Questionnaire

Discover how much you have learned.

Read and review the information in this book before using the multiple choice questionnaire to check your knowledge. There are 50 questions to answer. A score of 40 or more correct answers demonstrates satisfactory understanding of the enabling knowledge relating to the eight core units of the Level 3 NVQ/SVQ in Care Award.

For each question circle the answer which is MOST correct,

1. Empathy involves:
   a) accurately perceiving the feelings of others
   b) providing sympathy to others
   c) feeling sorry for others
   d) helping others

2. Advocacy involves:
   a) taking people to court
   b) speaking up on behalf of others
   c) obtaining goods for others
   d) talking about another person

3. Which of the following should NOT be included in an equal opportunities policy?
   a) examples of unlawful discrimination
   b) commitment to removing barriers to equal opportunity
   c) details of how the policy is to be carried out
   d) percentage of managers who are female and ethnic minorities

4. Which of the following is NOT a characteristic of institutionalisation?
   a) rigidity of routine
   b) occurs in large institutions only
   c) block treatment
   d) depersonalisation

5. Which of the following characteristics is NOT a sign of dehumanisation?
   a) resentment of harsh or unfair treatment
   b) lack of interest in the future
   c) lack of attention to personal hygiene
   d) loss of interest in things and events

6. Which of the following is poor practice when offering choices to clients:
   a) Stick to your promises.
   b) Provide clear explanations if requests cannot be granted.
   c) If you have concerns about offering choices, make the choice yourself.
   d) Be specific with your options.

7. Which of the following is NOT a human right?

   a) recognition as a person before law

   b) education

   c) going to church

   d) right to life

8. Which of the following is NOT a legal right enshrined in the Mental Health Act?

   a) having property protected

   b) entering into marriage

   c) voting

   d) obtaining a divorce

9. Which of the following is NOT a care service for which people have a right, in the community?

   a) domiciliary and day care services

   b) full assessment of needs

   c) home visits by a general practitioner

   d) practical support for families who care for relatives at home

10. Which of the following is NOT an existing right under the Patients' Charter?

    a) have any complaint about the NHS investigated

    b) be registered with a general practitioner

    c) be given a clear explanation of proposed treatment

    d) have access to your own health records

11. Which of the following is NOT a standard under the Patients' Charter?

    a) ensuring that everybody has access to available services

    b) not cancelling operations during the week of operation

    c) immediate assessment in the Accident and Emergency Department

    d) named nurse responsible for each patient

12. Which of the following is NOT a way of supporting individual beliefs?

    a) being sensitive to each person's needs

    b) addressing people by their preferred names and titles

    c) being respectful of other people's customs

    d) speaking a foreign language

13. Which of the following is NOT a way to build good relationships?

    a) dressing smartly

    b) knocking before entering a person's room

    c) introducing yourself when you enter a person's room

    d) being courteous and respectful to visitors

14. Which of the following is the most powerful non-verbal communicator?

    a) touch

    b) posture

    c) facial expression

    d) distance

15. Which of the following is NOT a barrier to communication?

    a) appearing bored or impatient

    b) using multiple questions

    c) negating or devaluing a person

    d) unconditional positive regard

16. Assault is:

    a) an aggressive defamatory statement

    b) mental or physical abuse or neglect

    c) an attack where a blow is delivered

    d) an unlawful personal attack

17. Paranoia is:

    a) delusions of persecution

    b) a mental illness

    c) a disliking of crowded places

    d) aversion to the unexpected

18. Which of the following is NOT a specific sign of physical abuse?

    a) multiple bruises and bruises of different ages

    b) fractures

    c) oval bruises with a gap at each side

    d) several small burns 1 - 1 1/2 centimetres across

19. Which of the following characteristics of a care environment increases the incidence of challenging behaviour?

    a) busy care environment

    b) locally-based care services

    c) crowded and hot waiting rooms

    d) working in care teams

20. Which of the following is NOT a way of caring for people at-risk?

    a) Report signs and symptoms of abuse immediately.

    b) Liaise with other care agencies involved in providing care.

    c) Include a broad outline in the care plan for the level of supervision that is needed.

    d) Point out the legal implications of the abuse to the abuser.

21. De-escalation is:

    a) techniques to escape the grip of an attacker

    b) tactics that calm down an aggressor

    c) techniques for handling extremely aggressive behaviour

    d) ignoring abusive behaviour

22. Which of the following personal behaviours help prevent aggression?

    a) Treat people with respect and dignity.

    b) Be honest with people.

    c) Maintain personal control of feelings.

    d) Ignore people's bad behaviour.

23. Which of the following is not an assertion technique for handling aggressive behaviour?

    a) self-disclosure

    b) confrontation

    c) partial agreement

    d) side-stepping

24. How can you avoid violence when making home visits?

    a) Take an escort if you are unsure about the safety of a visit.

    b) Leave your itinerary at the office.

    c) Ensure you wear your uniform.

    d) Arrange to be contacted if you are late returning.

25. Which of the following tactics is NOT appropriate in the face of violence?

    a) Confront the person.

    b) Relax and evenly balance your weight in readiness for rapid movement.

    c) Consider escape options.

    d) Use diversionary tactics.

26. For which of the following reasons is restraint NOT usually necessary?

    a) physical assault

    b) severe verbal abuse

    c) destructive behaviour

    d) self-harm

27. Which of the following is NOT necessary prior to restraint?

    a) Identify one person to take charge.

    b) Assess the situation while help is gathering.

    c) Preferably, carry out the restraint with no fewer than four staff.

    d) Prepare yourself for physical contact.

28. Which of the following should you NOT always do during restraint?

    a) Grab the hair to prevent biting.

    b) Keep talking to the person.

    c) Be committed to the restraint.

    d) Arrange for care after the restraint.

29. Aphasia is:

    a) difficulty in using and understanding words

    b) difficulty in speaking clearly

    c) difficulty in adjusting the tone of voice

    d) inability to speak

30. Communication reception is NOT:

    a) concentration span

    b) ability to discriminate

    c) affected by previous learning

    d) ability to remember

31. Communication expression does NOT consist of:

    a) articulation and modulation

    b) ability to interpret non-verbal communication

    c) interpersonal skills

    d) ability to listen

32. Which of the following strategies should NOT be used for people who suffer from aphasia?

    a) Use communication aids.

    b) Eliminate unnecessary noise.

    c) Encourage the person to speak faster.

    d) Be supportive and positive.

33. Which of the following strategies should NOT be used for people who have impaired hearing?

    a) Shout only when necessary.

    b) Use gestures where appropriate.

    c) Maintain eye contact.

    d) Ask for feedback.

34. When caring for a hearing aid you should NEVER:

    a) Clean the hearing aid with water.

    b) Turn off the hearing aid when not in use.

    c) Always use a case for storage.

    d) Remove the batteries if the hearing aid is not to be used for 24 hours or more.

35. Crisis refers to:

    a) an unpleasant emotional experience linked to annoyance, dread, and anxiety

    b) a period of time when a stressful situation is overwhelming

    c) a divorce or a bereavement of a close family member

    d) a day when you cannot cope

36. Which of the following is NOT usually a major stressor?

    a) divorce

    b) redundancy

    c) traffic jam

    d) death of a close relative

37. Which of the following is NOT a personal factor in the perception of stress?

    a) values

    b) personal goals

    c) personality

    d) control over stressors

38. Which of the following effects on health is least likely to be caused by stress?

    a) high blood pressure

    b) haemorrhoids

    c) stomach ulcer

    d) insomnia

39. Which of the following is NOT an essential feature of a crisis?

    a) crisis that peaks over a short period of time

    b) a triggering stress event

    c) feelings of loss, danger, or humiliation

    d) disruption of routine

40. Which of the following forms of help should NOT be given during a crisis?

    a) Provide emotional support.

    b) Provide companionship.

    c) Encourage the person to keep him/herself occupied.

    d) Encourage practical help.

41. When a person is in the denial stage of grief, which of the following should you NOT do?:

    a) Try to force the person to face the truth.

    b) Give the person time to adjust.

    c) Listen when the person wants to talk.

    d) Avoid forcing conversation.

42. Which of the following is NOT a pre-requisite for non-directive, client-centred counselling?

    a) empathy

    b) congruence

    c) non-possessive warmth

    d) not forcing conversations

43. Domiciliary services are usually provided by:

    a) National Health Service

    b) Social Services

    c) voluntary sector

    d) private sector

44. Which of the following is NOT a primary area for health promotion?

    a) diet

    b) alcohol consumption

    c) safe sex

    d) skin care

45. Which type of fire extinguisher can be used for most fires (except liquids and live electrical equipment)?

    a) powder

    b) foam

    c) water

    d) halon

46. Which of the following is not a type of client transfer?

    a) passive transfer

    b) active transfer

    c) complementary transfer

    d) assistive transfer

47. Which of the following is not a sign of infection?

    a) high blood pressure

    b) fever

    c) swelling

    d) discharge of pus

48. Which of the following is NOT the appropriate first aid for bleeding?

    a) Lay the casualty down and treat for shock.

    b) Always apply direct pressure to a wound.

    c) Secure a sterile unmedicated dressing over the wound.

    d) Never apply indirect pressure to stop the bleeding for more than 15 minutes at a time.

49. If a casualty's breath smells of pear drops, this is a sign of:

   a) generalised tonic-clonic seizure

   b) a fractured rib

   c) hypoglycaemia

   d) hyperglycaemia

50. According to the Data Protection Act, personal data must NOT be:

   a) obtained fairly and squarely

   b) made available to anybody on request

   c) held only for lawful purposes

   d) kept no longer than is necessary

Answers to Multiple Choice Questionnaire

41. a	42. d	43. b	44. d	45. c	46. c	47. a	48. b	49. d	50. b
31. b	32. c	33. a	34. a	35. b	36. c	37. d	38. b	39. a	40. c
21. b	22. d	23. b	24. a	25. a	26. b	27. c	28. a	29. a	30. d
11. b	12. d	13. a	14. c	15. d	16. d	17. a	18. b	19. c	20. c
1. a	2. b	3. d	4. b	5. a	6. c	7. c	8. d	9. c	10. a

Glossary of Terms

A

abuse	mental, physical, sexual, medical, or financial abuse, exploitation, or neglect
acidosis	disturbance of normal metabolism that causes body fluids to become more acid than normal
advocate	someone who speaks up on behalf of, and for the benefit of, another person.
angina	severe, but temporary attack of cardiac pain, usually caused by exercise in people with heart disease
antibody	specific substances produced in the blood, in response to being in contact with foreign protein, that have a role in the development of immunity
aphasia	difficulty using or understanding words
articulation	ability to speak clearly
assault	an unlawful personal attack
assertiveness	ability to express personal views in a clear, confident, and direct manner, without denying the rights of others
audit	formal inspection and assessment for the purposes of reporting and making recommendations

B

battery	an attack where an actual blow is delivered
break-away	techniques that allow a person to escape the grip of a violent attacker

C

challenging behaviour	problem behaviour that is demanding and disruptive which makes it difficult to provide quality support and care
control and restraint	techniques that use minimum force as a last resort for handling extremely aggressive behaviour
crepitus	sound when two broken ends of a bone scrape together
crisis	point in time when an urgent and stressful situation overwhelms a person

D

data	accumulated information or facts
de-escalation	tactics that aim to calm an aggressor
defamation	falsehoods (libel or slander) that result in damage to a person's reputation or character
depersonal-isation	an effect on a person of an institutionalised environment in which there is little opportunity for individual expression (e.g., lack of personal possessions, no privacy)
discrimination	perceived differences (usually showing a preference) between alternatives
disinfection	destruction of the majority of micro-organisms on inanimate objects by the use of a disinfectant

E

empathy — ability to accurately perceive the feelings of another, and the ability to communicate that understanding to the person

epidemiology — scientific study of distribution of diseases

F

false documentation — entries in a personal record that are not true

H

halo effect — tendancy to conform to others' expectations

hives — rash similar to that caused by nettles

hyperglycaemia — higher than normal level of glucose in the blood

hypoglycaemia — lower than normal level of glucose in the blood

I

institutionalisation — an effect on a person who lives in an environment where there is rigidity of routine, block treatment, depersonalisation, and little opportunity to express individuality

K

ketones — substances produced by incomplete metabolism, which can cause acidosis

L

label — classifying word or phrase that identifies something

lethargy — state of listlessness and lack of energy

libel — written, defamatory statement

M

mental defence mechanism — mental distortion of fact to protect oneself from stressful thoughts and feelings

micro-organism — living organism that can only be seen with a microscope (e.g., bacteria, viruses, some fungi, etc.)

modulation — adjustments and regulation of the tone of voice during conversation

N

negligence — failure to give assigned care, or giving improper care that causes harm (such as failure to raise bed rails, resulting in someone falling out of bed)

non-compliance — refusal to do what one has been asked to do

non-verbal communication — aspects of communication that are not spoken, often referred to as body language (i.e., facial expression, gestures, posture, eye contact, touch)

O

oedema — abnormal swelling of tissues due to retention of fluid

ophthalmic — pertaining to the eye

P

paranoia — delusions (false perceptions) of persecution

prejudice — an unfavourable opinion formed without proper judgement

S

seizure	abnormal functioning of the brain, often including loss of consciousness, caused by abnormal electrical discharges within the brain
self-disclosure	divulging personal information to another person
significant other	relative, friend, or anyone who is important to another person
slander	a spoken, defamatory statement
stereotype	characteristics which are held to be common to members of a category
sterilisation	process of killing all living micro-organisms usually by heat treatment
stigma	unpleasant or disgraceful characteristics attached to a person or group of people
stress	unpleasant emotional experience linked to dread, anxiety, annoyance, etc.
stroke	condition where damage to the brain has impaired the function of one side of the body

T

therapeutic relationship	enabling relationship in which a carer helps another person to meet his or her own needs
tranquilliser	drug that has a sedative and calming effect
tumour	swelling caused by a mass of abnormal tissue which resembles normal tissue, but fulfills no useful function and can be harmful

U

unconditional positive regard	relationship in which warmth, acceptance, and empathy are freely given

V

verbal communication	refers to spoken communication (e.g., words, language, tone of voice)
violence	force, severe threat, or serious abuse, including severe verbal abuse or threat thought likely to turn into violence, serious or persistent harassment, threat with a weapon, major or minor injury

Index

Index